How-To Hydroponics
4th Edition
Keith Roberto

This book is dedicated to my family,

friends and everyone who has been an

inspiration along the way.

First edition published 1994
Second edition published 1997
Third edition published 1999
Fourth edition published 2004

Reprinted 9/2014

www.howtohydroponics.com

All text, images and illustrations
Copyright 1994-2014 Keith Roberto
info@howtohydroponics.com
Cover design by Marissa Morris

ISBN - 0-9672026-1-2

Published by:
Electron Alchemy, Inc.
www.electronalchemy.com
Massapequa, New York 11762

Foreword

How-To Hydroponics, the fourth edition, represents the largest and most concise body of work I've accomplished on the subject of hydroponics thus far. So much has changed as technology and man's understanding of the science has progressed over the years, that I felt compelled to produce this new edition to keep my readers up to date and to further inspire others to give hydroponics a try. How-To Hydroponics has been written in an easy to follow style that combines a basic yet comprehensive background in the science of hydroponics with the hands-on experience that makes learning fun. Whether you grow for fun, food or profit, this completely revised edition covers everything you'll need to know to develop a working knowledge of the technology.

You'll learn, step-by-step, how to build and operate all the hydroponic and aeroponic systems detailed for construction in the book. You'll learn how to grow your favorite flowers, herbs and veggies with this exciting technology that is revolutionizing the agricultural industry. How-To Hydroponics Fourth Edition encompasses over a decade of research and development in the field of hydroponics. I have spared no expense to provide you with all the knowledge you'll need to get growing quickly and successfully with hydroponics. Every effort has been made to ensure that all the known questions and discrepancies from previous editions have been answered and corrected in this edition. Of course I'm only human, so if you find something I've missed, please let me know! My email is included on this page.

For best results, I recommend that you read this book in the order it has been written so as not to miss any important info that could sacrifice the quality of your results. Take the time to read this book entirely before beginning any type of planning or construction. The important information within will certainly affect your decisions of what, where and how to grow, and it will ultimately improve your chances for success.

Best Regards,
Keith Roberto

Contents

Plants For Food & Pharmacy

In addition to being one of the world's favorite foods, the tomato contains Lycopene, a natural carotenoid that is responsible for its red color. Lycopenes and other antioxidants can help prevent cellular damage and abnormal cellular growth. This was my first harvest of the year (on May 15th!) from my new backyard greenhouse that I'll show you how to build later on.

Plants are Mother Nature's ultimate factories. Powered by light from the sun, plants combine the earth's most basic chemical elements with water and gases in the air to create food and energy for growth. They not only feed themselves, but just about every other living organism on the food chain, including us. Much of modern medicine is also based upon botanical extracts and compounds found only in plants. In fact, the sciences of phytochemistry and pharmacognosy are all about making medicines from plants. In addition, almost every manufacturer in the health and beauty business uses botanical extracts to help their products nourish our skin and hair.

You Are What You Eat

Throughout my career in hydroponics, this is the one message that has always stayed with me. I've witnessed this phrase unfold before me every time I've planted a seed and harvested a fruit. The care that goes into cultivating that plant is mirrored in what comes out of it, so feed and care for your plants well, especially if you plan to eat them! If you're a computer geek like me, you may recall an old saying "GIGO," which means "garbage in, garbage out." Ring a bell? It's also true when growing plants.

So why start a book on hydroponics on an old adage? Simply because it's the most fundamental lesson you will ever learn when it comes to growing, and perhaps even the quality of your own life as well. As a food factory, a plant must have an endless supply of quality raw materials for it to continue manufacturing new stem, leaf, flowers and fruit that we see as growth. If any one of the required raw materials runs out , the entire manufacturing process will be affected or even interrupted completely. GIGO! And to further complicate matters, just as a human appetite changes as you grow, so does that of plants. Since plants are not as mobile as humans, satisfying their changing appetite is far more difficult in nature than it is for us with a market on every corner. As a result, plants have adapted to the environment and climates they inhabit. And in many cases, they have sacrificed their own genetic potential in doing so. For instance, if a plant is admired for its flavor and it is relocated to another environment, the stress may cause the plant to reduce the oils responsible for its savory taste. If this stress continues, as the plant breeds it will adapt to overcome the environmental stress in future generations, and this adaptation may very well result in a healthy, but flavorless variant.

Hydroponics To The Rescue

In order for any plant to reach its full genetic potential of producing the beautiful foliage, flowers or fruit its programmed to create, it must be provided with everything it needs in just the right proportions, and, at just the right time. With the science of hydroponics, this is possible by applying proper watering and feeding regimens, environmental control and plenty of quality lighting. While the literal meaning of hydroponics is nothing more than feeding plants while irrigating (U.S. farmers call it "fertigation"), its definition has expanded to include all the aspects mentioned above as they apply to growing the perfect plant. While the definition of the hydroponics has expanded, misinformation also persists. Many people still believe hydroponically grown plants are fed "steroids" or other dangerous chemicals to force them to grow so well. In fact, hydroponic growers are simply "allowing" plants to reach their full genetic potential by carefully providing for their needs as nature is sometimes unable to do.

The idea of growing a perfect plant has different meanings for different people. For instance, an orchid fanatic may define the perfect plant as being of a certain rare variety, color or symmetry. For a commercial tomato grower, the perfect plant may be a variety that grows fast, resists disease and yields tasty fruit with a long shelf life. The orchid grower isn't looking to produce orchids in the same fashion as the tomato grower. But in both instances, by applying the principles you will learn in this book, both can achieve unrivaled success by using hydroponics.

While hydroponics provides each grower with the ability to help his or her plants achieve their full growth potential, you must be aware of the one aspect that is beyond the control of all growers: genetics. A poor variety of tomato that lacks flavor when grown in the field will likely lack flavor when grown

Seed Terms

Open Pollinated means seeds produced by plants unsegregated according to favorable or unfavorable genetics. Most common vegetables and flowers are open pollinated since the varieties have generally become indigenous to the locale where they are grown and prosper well.

F_1 Hybrid seeds are carefully produced by cross breeding two pure bred parents. Increased vigor, equal height, shape color and yield can be expected from hybrid plants. For the commercial producer, hybrids have the additional advantage of maturing at the same time to increase harvest efficiency.

Home grown seed is generally collected from local gardens that have produced fruit and flowers from which the seed is saved. F_1 hybrids will generally not breed true this way which will leave you with an unpredictable crop at best.

The Aloe Vera plant produces plantlets in a radial fashion around the mother plant. Each of these plantlets can be replanted and in turn will produce even more aloe plants in time. Because of Aloe's proven benefits to human skin, there is a lot of commercial interest in hydroponic production of Aloe Vera.

hydroponically as well. It may grow twice as fast and yield three times the weight, but if flavor is your fancy, you won't be happy. Fortunately, finding top quality seed isn't difficult, and with a little research you can find the varieties that will give you exactly what you want out of your hydroponic garden. In fact, you may already have the particular strain on hand, or growing at a friend o relative's house nearby.

It Starts With A Seed

If you think of a plant as being like a movie script, or perhaps even a computer program, you can better see how its life unfolds according to a predetermined chain of events. We call this chain of events the "stages of growth," and each of these stages can be triggered by internal or external stimuli. For plants, it all starts with a seed, which after sprouting becomes a seedling, and eventually becomes a mature plant capable of reproducing itself by creating new seeds. Note that when plants reach their

Don't let all this talk about seeds scare you. You'll learn how to create new plants from your current favorites by "cloning," which is nothing more than taking a fresh shoot and rooting it so it can become an independent plant of its own.

All plants start from seeds. While many plants can be propagated by taking cuttings, most growers begin by planting some seeds and marvelling as they unfold into mature plants. The diagram shows how a seed planted just below the ground level first splits its case upon absorbing water, drops a root which grows downward with gravity and then breaks surface forcing forward its first set of leaves as the husk drops away.

reproductive stage, external genetic material is introduced which may ever so slightly, or even drastically influence the "program" of the next generation. This is how plants breed outdoors in their natural state. By growing plants indoors, breeders can control which plants exchange genetic material with each other to influence the outcome in a particular way that is beneficial for the breeder. For instance, if a tomato grower likes a particular tasting tomato, but finds it grows too slowly, he may "cross" it with a more rapidly maturing variety to speed up the process in future generations. I don't want to get too deep into the subject of breeding at this point, but I must stress that even with the most advanced hydroponic methods, garbage in = garbage out. So choose your stock carefully!

Whether you are growing for food, fun or profit, choosing the right varieties will make as much a difference to your success, and ultimate enjoyment as applying all the technology in this book. For a quick real-life example, the basket of tomatoes shown in the beginning of this chapter were grown from seeds given to me by a fellow grower in California. I asked for a sweet and salty tomato that would do well in a greenhouse, which means it had to be self pollinating. I grew a tomato (Matusalah) that my entire family and immediate neighborhood is raving about to this day. In fact, they were so good and grew so well I've kept the same plant alive through several seasons as a mother plant from which I regularly take cuttings to start new plants. Last November I counted 41 tomatos on the six plants I raised aeroponically which turned out to be perfect stocking stuffers for the holiday! Login to howtohydroponics.com/interactive/ to continue learning and enjoy preferred pricing on all that makes your garden grow.

"Even with the most advanced hydroponic methods, garbage in still equals garbage out, so choose your seeds and cutting stock carefully!"

Bright white roots are a sign of a healthy seedling. Baby Lettuce at 12 days from germination in "Perfect Starts," a brand of organic starter sponges that helps to speed germination and reduce the occurence of transplant shock.

What Is Hydroponics?

"One could not imagine a world without water, as one would not exist to imagine"

Without water, life on earth would not exist. There would be no hydroponics, much less a culture to practice it. Water is a vital part of every living cell. In plants, it provides turgor pressure on cell walls to keep leaves from wilting. And it transports nutrition and energy stores in the form of dissolved salts and sugars throughout the plant. This book is about water, focusing on how to distribute it, maintain its quality, and enrich it with the nutrition vital to plant life. In nature, fire and water act together to recharge the soil with nutrients. When forests burn, wood is turned to ash. Wood ash is rich in Potassium, one of the plant kingdom's fundamental foods. When the rains come, lifeless leaves and fallen branches are helped along their path to decay. Animals and insects hasten this process through their consumption of plant materials and excretion of organic wastes which filter down into the soil below. The organic matter in the soil is biologically decomposed into the basic nutrient salts that plants feed on. The falling rains once again help in dissolving these salts, making them available for plants to absorb through their roots. For a plant to receive a well balanced diet, everything in nature must be in perfect harmony. Forests must burn, animals must eat, rains must come, wood must rot, and microbes in the soil must be present and ready to go to work. Rarely, if ever, can you find such ideal conditions occurring on a regular basis. In fact, the earth's rainforests may be the only remaining examples of near perfect botanical conditions. Visit one if you ever get the chance! I certainly plan to.

Now that we have a better understanding of the natural growing process, we can see that hydroponics is all about enriching water with the very same nutritive salts found in nature. It's about creating and maintaining a "nutrient solution" that is perfectly balanced for your plants. Most hydroponic systems contain the nutrient solution in a closed system. This helps protect it from evaporation and from discharging into our environment as does the runoff from exposed, fertilized soil. This conservative approach to water management makes hydroponics the method of choice in drought-stricken areas worldwide, and as a result, it is rapidly becoming known as "Earth Friendly Gardening."

Since you will be practicing the art and science of "water gardening", it is a wise idea to know what your local water contains. Contact your local water company and ask for their water quality analysis. If your water comes from a well, you will most likely have to send it out to a lab for analysis on your own. The most important factor affecting water quality is its relative "hardness" or "softness." Hard water means that there is a lot of dissolved mineral content, primarily calcium carbonate, which is often seen as scale on hot water pipes. Soft water is generally very pure or low in dissolved solids. Distilled (or deionized) water, or water that has been through a reverse osmosis filter, are all considered soft. Most commercially available hydroponic nutrients are made for soft water. However, if you have hard water, there are some nutrient products made for hard water as well.

A Brief History Of Hydroponics

Truly a wonder of modern science, hydroponic gardens now produce bountiful harvests of fruit, vegetables, grains, herbs and flowers in places never before able to sustain growth. Hydroponic gardens grow the healthiest crops with the highest yields and vitamin content, thanks to their perfectly balanced nutrient solutions and growing environments. Modern hydroponic methods provide food for millions of people worldwide, supplying us with superior quality produce, even out of season. Even with all its advantages, the American consumer is sometimes wary of hydroponically grown produce. Many years ago, hydroponic products were admittedly of poor quality, and this association still persists for some people. This old association is rapidly changing because hydroponic produce has evolved into a superior quality, premium product. In fact, modern day hydroponic cultivation has become so effective, NASA itself has devised an advanced method of hydroponics for use in outer space. While it may appear that hydroponics is a recent invention, its history can be traced back to the dawn of civilization.

The science of hydroponics began with experiments to determine the elementary composition of plants. These experiments have been dated as early as 1600 A.D. In addition, historical records reveal plants have been cultivated in soil free mixtures of sand and gravel much earlier than that. The hanging

To this day, many people are still unaware of the art and science of hydroponics, even though most of us have practiced it first hand by placing cut flowers in a vase of water and adding a little plant food.   Photo: Basil cutting rooting in water.

Hydroponic Benefits

1. *Elimination of soil borne pests, fungi and diseases.*

2. *Elimination of troublesome weeds and stray seedlings which eliminates the need for herbicides and reduces labor..*

3. *Reduction of health risks and labor costs associated with pest management and soil care.*

4. *Reduced turn around time between planting as no soil preparation is required.*

5. *Significantly increased yields and shorter crop maturation cycle.*

gardens of Babylon and the floating gardens of the Mexican Aztecs are both examples of early hydroponic gardening. Historians have found Egyptian hieroglyphics depicting the cultivation of plants in water that can be dated as far back as several thousand years, BC!

The word "Hydroponics" was coined by Dr. W.F. Gericke in 1936 to describe the cultivation of both edible and ornamental plants in a solution of water and dissolved nutrients. The simple meaning is derived from the Greek "Hydro," meaning water, and "Ponos," meaning labor. In this method of cultivation, plants are provided with the nutrients required for growth by a "nutrient solution," which is simply water that's been enriched with dissolved essential elements. In a hydroponic garden, this nutrient solution can be circulated around the roots by either the passive force of gravity, or by the active force of an electromechanical pump. Some systems bathe the roots in nutrient solution and use an air pump to oxygenate the solution from below, this helps to prevent stagnation and provides roots with much needed oxygen.

Plants grown hydroponically are generally healthier than their soil-grown counterparts. They receive a near-perfectly balanced diet, and rarely come in contact with soil borne pests and diseases. Super-efficient hydroponic systems, like the ones I'll show you how to build later in the book, conserve water and nutrients by preventing evaporation and runoff. Arid regions where water is scarce can now grow crops using hydroponics. Since hydroponic systems deliver water and nutrients directly to the plants, crops can be grown closer together without starving each other, and healthier plants also contribute to higher yields. By growing crops in a clean environment, under ideal conditions, hydroponics saves the costs of soil preparation, insecticides, fungicides and losses due to drought and ground flooding. When grown outdoors in soil, plants expend a tremendous amount of energy developing a large root system to search for moisture and nutrients. When grown hydroponically, their roots are directly bathed or sprayed with nutrients dissolved in water. Since they no longer need to search for food, most of their energy can be redirected into the production of foliage, flowers, fruits and vegetables. Plants grown hydroponically are healthier because they receive a well-balanced "diet." They are more vigorous because little energy is diverted into searching for water and nutrients. As a result, hydroponically grown produce is usually larger, tastier, and more nutritious than the same produce grown in soil. In order to give the physical support that soil would normally provide, a clean, sterile medium such as sand, gravel, rocks, coco fiber or rockwool (or combination of each) may be used. In the case of aeroponics, there is no medium, plants receive physical support from baskets and even wires suspended from the roof (see Disney's Epcot Center photo). At Epcot, plants are rotated through a chamber that supplies their roots with a fine mist of water and nutrients. The extra Oxygen that reaches the roots substantially increases the plant's metabolism.

Current Research

At the Environmental Research Laboratory (ERL) at the University of Arizona in Tucson, Dr. Carl Hodges and Dr. Merle Jensen, in conjunction with Walt Disney Productions, have developed new concepts for presenting hydroponic technologies to the public as entertainment to enhance learning. The ERL helped create "Listen to The Land" and "Tomorrow's Harvest," which are now major facilities at Epcot Center near Orlando, Florida. While many currently believe the practice of hydroponics is "futuristic," as we have seen, the way of the future has been through a long history that can be traced back to man's first attempts at agriculture. Another point worth mentioning is that while the term "hydroponics" describes the specific method of cultivating plants in water, more often the term is being used to describe a mindset whereby all aspects of the cultivation process are carefully monitored and adjusted to provide the optimum growing environment. With its extensive scientific resources, there is no better organization than NASA to provide us with a glimpse of what is possible when an ideal environment can be created for growing plants.

Aeroponically grown squash plants at Disney's Epcot Center hang from an overhead cable that transports them through a misting chamber where their roots receive the nutrient solution.

What All Gardeners Can Learn From NASA

Hydroponics is NASA's solution to providing space travellers with a self-sufficient food source. The Administration has sponsored a research program titled Controlled Ecological Life Support System (CELSS) in order to further develop the technology and carry it into the future. The picture at right is of Epcot/NASA's Space Agriculture expo as seen from a tour of the Epcot Center attraction. The lighting used in these

Photo from Epcot Center's "Tomorrow's Harvest" tour depicts how NASA envisions growing lettuce in outer space.

examples is high-pressure sodium or HPS, which is the choice for most commercial growers due to its strong "lumen per watt" efficiency. High Intensity Discharge (H.I.D.) lighting, which includes the HPS and metal halide (MH) type lamps, is the best lighting to use when gardening indoors or supplementing natural lighting due to their efficiency and close representation of the sun's color and intensity. Whether or not this technology is ever actually used in space travel, what NASA has learned from developing these self-sufficient food source programs can be used to great advantage by every gardener willing to give it a try!

It's All About The Roots

Root systems vary in size from those of a seedling, perhaps a few inches long, to those of a 300' redwood that can grow larger in size than the visible tree itself! Regardless of the physical size of the plant, roots serve three essential functions: (1) the uptake of water and nutrients; (2) storage for manufactured materials; (3) providing physical support for the plant above ground. Hydroponics is all about healthy roots! The absorption of water and nutrients takes place just behind the root tip through tiny root hairs. These root hairs are extremely delicate and usually die off as the root tip grows further into the medium. The method in which the roots absorb water and nutrients is called diffusion. In this process, water and oxygen pass into the root structure through membranes in the cell walls. An interesting point is that diffusion actually takes place at the ionic level, which in laymen's terms means nutritional elements are passed by the electrical exchange of charged particles. This fact can lead to confusion over whether hydroponics is unnatural and is not at the level of "organic quality" because plants grown using hydroponic methods are not fed "organic nutrients." The true bottom line is that roots can ONLY uptake PURE ELEMENTS, no matter what the original source is. In other words, in the process of feeding, plants can't absorb organic material unless it is first broken down into pure elements, no matter where it comes from. Since a hydroponic system is generally cleaner than a composted organic growing environment, the hydroponic system itself provides a superior growing environment. But also remember the first principle of hydroponics: GIGO. Garbage in, garbage out. A hydroponics system is only as good as the nutrient its fed with.

When thinking about plant roots, oxygen is rarely the first thing that comes to mind. But oxygen is crucial to root health. Oxygen is absorbed by roots and then utilized for growth, and

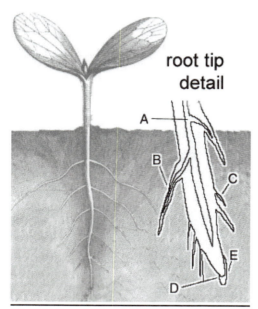

(A) Fluid Vessel (B) Lateral Root (C) Root Hairs
(D) Growth Zone (E) Root Cap

The author poses besides a 300 ft. tall Redwood whose roots spread just as far below the surface to provide food and support for the massive tree.

in return, the roots give off Carbon Dioxide. The absence of oxygen in the root zone will cause asphyxiation, which in turn will damage the roots and will adversely affect the top of the plant as well. Stagnation of water in the root zone also causes asphyxiation, in addition to root rot. Once plant roots die, or they become dehydrated, death of the organism is usually imminent. Many studies have proven that oxygenation to the root zone is a major factor in determining a plant's growth potential. In fact, the practice of "Aeroponics" as a growing method has been developed to maximize growth one step beyond that conventionally believed to be possible with hydroponics. Plants grown aeroponically actually have their roots suspended midair!

Aeroponics teaches us that plants can function normally with their roots exposed to light, provided they are always at 100% relative humidity. However, exposure to light also promotes the growth of algae. Algae appears as a green or brown slime on roots, plumbing, and containers. Some studies have suggested that plants suffer when their roots are exposed to light, however this is probably mostly due to the resulting algae growth on the surface of the root. Algae will compete for both water and nutrients, as well as oxygen. To be on the safe side, I recommend using opaque containers and avoid the use of transparent materials for tubing and reservoirs, for any hydroponic system. Dark colors such as deep green, deep blue and black work best at blocking stray light. You should also note that plant roots are extremely delicate and should not be handled.

You will, at some point, need to transplant seedlings or cuttings into your hydroponic garden. Just be patient and gentle, and keep roots wet. In the event that roots begin to obstruct proper flow and drainage in your system, you may have no choice but to adjust their position, which may cause damage if you are not careful. It's of utmost importance to maintain sufficient humidity around your plants' roots at all times. Low humidity will cause dehydration and root die back. However, you also do NOT want to leave your roots soaking in STAGNANT water, as this will cause the roots to die from lack of oxygen. Die back is visible in the form of dry, browned, and sometimes decaying roots. Once your plants' roots die, there is no method to revive them. If the damage is serious, your crop stands a slim chance of surviving. Login to howtohydroponics.com/interactive/ to continue learning and enjoy preferred pricing on all that makes your garden grow.

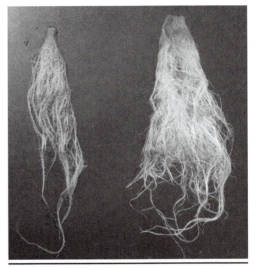

Roots at left are from a 45 day old hydroponic cucumber grown in a low quality nutrient solution. The roots at right were fed with a premium quality nutrient solution.

Air roots vs. water roots

Plants that are grown in soil and granular or fibrous growing mediums that maintain a high percentage of air to water develop air roots (below left). The tiny root hairs serve to steer growth in the direction of water and food. Note that plants grown with their roots completely submerged in water develop "water roots" (shown below right). Observe the absence of root hairs, which are unnecessary in this situation. While air rooted plants can easily be transplanted to a hydroponic system, water roots usually will not survive the move to soil or a drier medium. More on pg. 83

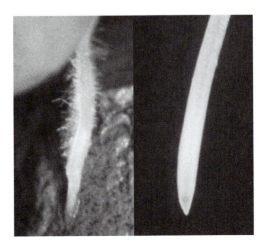

Hydroponic Mediums

In most hydroponic gardens, soilfree growing mediums are used primarily for starting seeds and when rooting cuttings. The less medium a system requires, the easier and less expensive it is to operate. This is a major consideration for those intending to make a profit from their hydroponic gardens. Modern day soilfree mediums have come a long way since the use of river gravel and sand in early systems. A perfect medium is able to hold a nearly equal concentration of air and water. As you have learned, your plants need both oxygen and nutrients to reach their roots. The water/air holding capacity of a growing medium is determined by the small spaces between each granule or fiber. These "holes" in the medium are known as "interstitial spaces."

Fine sand features very small interstitial spaces that cannot hold much air and water. On the other hand, coarse gravel has large interstitial spaces that can hold a lot of both air and water. Yet, as science would have it, once the interstitial space gets to be too large for capillary action to hold the water in place, you guessed it, the water runs right through it. If your system constantly re-circulates your nutrient solution, a fast draining medium would be acceptable. But obviously, coarse gravel isn't a good medium for a system that doesn't constantly circulate nutrient to the plants.

The Perfect Medium

1. *Holds a even ratio of air to water.*

2. *Helps to buffer pH changes over time.*

3. *Is easily flushed and re-wets easily after being completely dehydrated as would be the case during storage.*

3. *Is reusable or biodegradable to insure safe disposal.*

4. *Is inexpensive and easy to obtain.*

5. *Should be lightweight and easy to work with both indoors and out..*

Pictured from left to right are the most commonly used loose mediums for hydroponics; Coconut Coir, Agricultural Grade Perlite, Expanded Clay Pellets and Common Pea Gravel. Each of these mediums may be used alone or in combination with each other to enhance performance. For instance, Coco Coir is commonly mixed 50/50 with an equal volume of Perlite to provide a higher air holding ratio then Coir alone.

Coconut Coir

My favorite loose growing medium is coconut coir, otherwise known by trade names like Ultrapeat, Cocopeat and Coco-tek. Coco coir represents a major step forward in organic soilfree growing mediums. It combines the water retention of vermiculite with the air retention of perlite, however it is a completely organic medium made from shredded coconut husks. Why coconut husks? The coconut husk serves its seed two purposes: (1) protection from sun and salt while floating in the ocean; (2) a hormone-rich and fungus free medium to speed germination and rooting upon landfall. Finely shredded and steam sterilized, coconut coir offers plants an ideal rooting medium that also offers protection against root diseases and fungus. And unlike peat moss, which is rapidly becoming depleted from overuse, coir is a completely renewable resource. You can now find several variations of coir on the market. The most popular is the compressed briquette format, which requires soaking in a gallon of water before use. During soaking, the coir re-hydrates, expanding up to six times the size of the original briquette, resulting in about 1/3 cu. ft. of loose coir with a consistency and color that most closely resembles fresh ground coffee. As an added benefit, coir doesn't soil your hands, clothes, or carpets. It brushes off readily, without any residue.

Cutaway view of tomato roots as they penetrate a 50/50 mix of coco-coir and perlite. Layer of perlite on bottom is to allow complete drainage in this top-fed hydroponic planter.

Perlite

Perlite has been around longer than any other soilfree growing medium. Made from air-puffed glass pellets, and nearly as light as air, perlite has excellent oxygen retention. Its ability to retain oxygen is the main reason it is used as a supplement in soil and soilfree mixes. The main drawback of perlite is its lightweight consistency, which makes it easy to get washed away. This drawback makes perlite an inappropriate medium in flood and flush type hydroponic systems or those that would be subjected to strong wind and rains if situated outdoors. An ultra-coarse grade of perlite, well suited for hydroponics, is marketed under the tradename Aerolite.

Close-up view of young tomato root as it grows into expanded clay aggregate. Inset shows inner porosity of LECA stone.

LECA

LECA stands for Lightweight Expanded Clay Aggregate and is an extremely coarse growing medium. Some of its common trade names include Geolite, Grorox and Hydroton. LECA is made of expanded clay pellets that hold water by virtue of its porosity and surface area. These mediums are pH neutral and reusable, making them ideal for hydroponic systems. While lava rocks appear to have some of the same qualities, they should never be used in hydroponic systems because they alter the pH and leave behind a heavy sediment that can harm equipment. For the same reason, you should always rinse new LECA stones to remove the dust caused by movement during shipment.

Perfect Starts

The latest breakthrough in growing mediums is the "molded" starter sponge made from organic compost and a flexible, biodegradable polymer binder. Available in several shapes and sizes, these innovative growing sponges solve the main problem growers face when wanting to use an organic medium in a hydroponic system. Namely, they do not fall apart or crumble during transplanting which serves to prevent damage to delicate roots. This is a significant advantage, because root damage that occurs during transplant is the leading cause of transplant shock. The starting sponges exhibit a perfect air to water holding ratio, and when used in conjunction with their plastic tray inserts, will guide roots to grow directly downward instead of spiraling, as is the case in many other types of starting trays. Since the plugs don't crumble, or break apart and clog delicate sprayers, Perfect Starts perform well in all types of hydroponic systems.

100% organic compost is molded into conveniently shaped starter plugs to offer the highest performance starting/rooting medium currently available.

Rockwool

Rockwool is made from molten rock that is spun into long, glass-like fibers. These fibers are then compressed into bricks and cubes, or sold loose as "flock." Rockwool has long been used to insulate buildings as an alternative to fiberglass, and has been a mainstay in commercial hydroponics for the last twenty years. It readily absorbs water and has decent drainage properties, which is why it is used widely as a starting medium for seeds and a rooting medium for cuttings. In my opinion, the premiere benefit of rockwool is its sterility from pathogens and just about anything else that could contaminate a hydroponic system. Some of the world's largest hydroponic greenhouses use rockwool slabs to raise numerous varieties of plants to full maturity, and they often reuse the rockwool slabs many times by steam sterilizing the slabs between crops.

Lately I have noticed a decline in the use of rockwool by the hydroponics hobbyist. From what I have observed, this may be due to a wider sense of environmental responsibility to avoid using products that cause pollution from their manufacturing process, as is the case with rockwool. A word of caution should you decide to work with rockwool. Many people find its dust is irritating to the skin, which leads me to believe there could be a similar effect in the lungs if its dust is inhaled. Login to howtohydroponics.com/interactive/ to continue learning and enjoy preferred pricing on all that makes your garden grow.

Rockwool - rockwool comes in cubes, slabs and loose bales. It has a very good air to water holding capacity and is used heavily by the commercial greenhouse industry.

Growcube rockwool is relatively new and delivers the same features of rockwool slabs and blocks but in a loose, sugarcube sized format.

Hydroponic Technology

A hydroponic system should be designed to fulfill the specific requirements of plants with the most reliable and efficient method(s) of nutrient delivery. The three major plant-requirements that a hydroponic system must satisfy are:

1) Provide roots with a fresh, well balanced supply of water and nutrients.
2) Maintain a high level of gas exchange between nutrient solution and roots.
3) Protect against root dehydration and immediate crop failure in the event of a pump failure or power outage.

Hydroponic systems can be either active or passive. An active system includes a mechanical means for re-circulating the nutrient solution, while a passive system relies on capillary action, absorption, and/or the force of gravity to replenish roots with nutrient. Besides being generally more efficient, and therefore more productive, a nice feature of active hydroponic systems is how easily they can be implemented in an automated greenhouse. The automation system does not have to be complicated to provide outstanding results. Just as a fan may be connected to a thermostat to control temperature, a timer may be connected to a to deliver nutrients to the plants as necessary. If such a system is designed properly, a large nutrient reservoir could feed the crop for weeks before needing a refill. In this scenario, as long as the system is reliable, the garden will continue to thrive indefinitely without the need for continual supervision.

For a hydroponic system to be considered reliable, we must insure that the three major plant requirements are met on a consistent basis. Efficiency is just as important because it will define your operating expenses, and in some cases can prevent disrupting the growing environment. The best way to build a reliable, efficient system is through intelligent engineering, combined with practical experience. Although the feats of modern engineers are quite incredible these days, sometimes complex problems are solved with even more complex solutions. Experience has proven simple solutions are usually the most reliable. So following the old US military dictum, Keep It Simple

21

Silly (KISS), can certainly help the hydroponic gardener achieve consistent, reliable results.

Now that we have a better understanding how a hydroponic system works, let's look at how some of the active hydroponic techniques currently in use today employ some of the same techniques of gardens used hundreds and even thousands of years ago. One of the earliest records of people using hydroponics describes the floating gardens of the Mexican Aztecs. These gardens were crafted similar to naturally occurring ponds, complete with water lilies and hyacinths. In natural ponds, plants obtain water and nutrition directly from the pond in a bioponic environment. Waste products from fish, birds and other animals provide a rich blend of organic nutrients for the microbes in the sand and mud to thrive on. The excrements of these microbes then provide the plants with the nutrients they need to thrive. Fresh water that falls from the sky in the form of precipitation replenishes the water that is transpired by plants and lost to evaporation. In the same way, aeration and circulation in the ancient water garden was provided by falling rain or running water. When the rain stopped falling, or the stream ran dry, these gardens would become stagnated and eventually dry up. For this reason, these early garden designers built sophisticated irrigation systems consisting of troughs that could supply water where it was needed most, and sometimes over great distances.

Sand And Gravel Culture

Although sand can be used as a growing medium with success, it has poor aeration qualities due to the small interstitial spaces between the grains. Remember, when choosing a soilfree medium for hydroponics, to look for good water holding capacity combined with good drainage qualities. This combination will ensure that your choice of mediums will allow the roots to feed, exhaust CO_2, and ingest Oxygen properly. Provided proper nutrient and water circulation is met, you'd be surprised at what mediums plants can be grown in. I once grew a plant in Styrofoam packing peanuts and we've all seen weeds growing from the cracks in cement sidewalks. Recent research has revealed the importance oxygen plays in the root zone. Oxygen is necessary for the plant to perform respiration, which provides the energy needed for the uptake of water and nutrient ions. These studies have proven that increased absorption of oxygen by the

This gravel culture system is an easy and inexpensive way to grow plants hydroponically. The large ring around these basil plants feeds them with a constant dripping action that's powered by a small air pump. General Hydroponics Power Grower shown.

The Dutch Bucket method works well for large, long term crops such as vine tomatoes, cucumbers and roses. Just about any type of growing media can be used including perlite, coconut coir, gravel and expanded clay pellets.

Greenhouse tomatoes growing in plastic sleeved rockwool slabs and fed by drip irrigation.

roots results in healthier, larger and faster growing crops. As the results of this research are released, new growing methods are being designed to apply these findings and improve production further.

The Dutch Bucket Method

This method is aptly named because it was first introduced in Holland and is now extensively used by commercial growers there for roses, tomatoes and cucumbers. The Dutch Bucket method allows the grower to use just about any growing medium, including coco-coir, perlite, LECA stone, gravel, and even sand. The Dutch Bucket is basically a 2.5 gallon bucket with a special drain fitting that maintains a small reserve of nutrient at the bottom as a precautionary measure. This method is best suited for large, long-term crops such as vine tomatoes, cucumbers and roses. Each bucket is fed nutrient solution independently by a single or double dripper, and it drains through the bucket into a common drain

tube made from 1.5 inch PVC pipe. The system's reservoir is positioned below the level of the drain pipe, and gravity carries the solution back to it. A pump then re-circulates the nutrient solution back to the drippers to start the feeding cycle over again. The inset photo details how each bucket has a small recess on its bottom that allows it to sit flush atop a drain pipe. Dutch Buckets can be spaced at just about any convenient interval, however the growers (and plants!) prefer no less than a 10" interval, on center.

The Rockwool Slab Drip System

The simplest and most common hydroponic method is using drip irrigation to deliver nutrient enriched water to plants grown in rockwool slabs. Many commercial tomato and pepper growers use this technique since it is relatively low-maintenance and can generally deliver foolproof results although it does produce runoff. In this photo, taken at Nipomo Mesa Farms in Santa Maria, CA, rows of tomato plants are supported by strings in a method called air-layering. As the fruit is harvested off the bottom of the plant using this method, the growing vines are coiled around each other much like a rope is coiled on the ground. Air layering allows single vine plants to reach 40 feet in length in some instances.

The Nutrient Film Technique (NFT)

The Nutrient Film Technique, or NFT, was pioneered by Allen Cooper at the Glasshouse Crops Research Institute in Littlehampton, England. In this growing technique, plants are placed atop an inverted 'V' shaped channel, sealed on all sides into a box-like tunnel, through which a thin film of nutrient solution passes along the bottom. A pump and reservoir combination situated below the channels collects and recycles the nutrient back through the system. Roots grow down along the channel, receiving oxygen directly from the inside of the trough, while receiving water and nutrients from the thin film of nutrient being carried along the bottom of the channel by gravity. The enclosed channels maintains 100% humidity to protect against dehydration. Excellent results can be obtained with this system. However, maintaining the "nutrient film" becomes difficult once the roots form large mats at the bottom of the channel. The resulting puddling can create stagnation in the root zone, depleting roots of oxygen and fresh nutrient. Efficiency, on the other hand, is excellent because the closed channel limits evaporation.

The nutrient film technique is most popular amongst lettuce growers as it is well suited to low growing crops with fast turnaround. Pictured here is a hybrid NFT system planted with ten day old lettuce.

The Raft System

The raft system is an interesting technique of growing lettuce and other short stature crops. In this method, plants are supported by baskets fit into Styrofoam sheets that float upon a bath of nutrient solution. The nutrient solution is circulated and aerated

Shown here is the lettuce raft system at Disney Epcot Center's "Listen to the Land"

The perfect system

1. *Has a simple, inexpensive design.*

2. *Is fully automated and requires as little day to day maintenance as possible.*

3. *Is geared for growing your choice of crops, for instance, the NFT system is perfect for Lettuce but not for Tomatoes.*

4. *Wastes almost no water and nutrients.*

5. *Provides your plants with exactly the right ratio of air and water to maximize growth.*

This healthy basil specimen was grown in a hybrid Ein Gedi system that utilized horizontally oriented, 4 in. PVC pipes as growth chambers. In the background are several varieties of lettuce that were grown in the same indoor system.

Aeroponics provides plant roots with maximum oxygenation for explosive growth - note the root density and bright white coloring indicative of a super healthy root system in an Aerospring.

from below to maintain a high level of dissolved oxygen and avoid stagnation. The raft system is a very economic means of producing large quantities of lettuce and mixed greens in no time.

Ein Gedi System

First developed in Ein Gedi Israel, hence the name, the Ein Gedi System (EGS) introduced a revolutionary new method to hydroponics. The system is comprised of fully enclosed rectangular growth chambers. Inside each container, nutrient solution is circulated 1-6 inches below evenly spaced mesh baskets that contain the plants. The air gap between the baskets and the solution is misted by sprayers residing along the upper inside edge of the chamber. Roots growing into the mist zone are subjected to intense oxygenation, resulting in vigorous development. Once the roots grow through the mist zone, they are greeted by a circulating bath of oxygenated nutrient solution that eliminates the problem of stagnation commonly associated with NFT. The EGS provides a quick and efficient method for developing seedlings and cuttings into large, healthy plants. The PVC systems I'll show you how to build later use this technique.

Aeroponics

The most recent technology to be developed in agriculture is Aeroponics, a method in which a plant's roots are fed and watered midair. The plants are generally suspended from baskets (similar to those in which strawberries are packaged) at the top of a closed trough or cylinder. With the plants suspended in this manner, all essential nourishment can be provided to the roots by spraying them with a nutrient solution. Since the roots are suspended in midair, they receive the maximum amount of oxygen possible. This method is also the most nutrient-efficient, because you need only provide what the plants require, and any nutrient that is not absorbed is drained back into the reservoir and recycled much like the previous methods. It is of utmost importance that the atmosphere in which the roots grow is maintained at 100% relative humidity to prevent dehydration.

A drawback to current aeroponic systems is maintaining root health in the event of pump malfunction or loss of power. Without the spray of nutrient enriched water, root systems will not remain healthy for long. They will rapidly dry up and die.

However, the increased oxygenation that is received by the plant's root structure benefits growth at an unprecedented level and has been scientifically proven to increase crop yields by as much as 10 times over soil. The AeroSpring design that is featured for construction later in the book combines aeroponics with a deep, reservoir to protect against crop loss in the event of a pump failure.

The AutoPot

Relatively new to the market here in the US is the AutoPot. A unique, self-feeding planter that has proven very reliable in commercial installations around the world. Within each AutoPot tray resides an "AQUAvalve" that automatically sub-irrigates plants with nutrient solution on demand. Since the AQUAvalve can be gravity fed, there is no need for pumps and timers This makes the AutoPot ideal for use in unsupervised locations or where access to electricity is limited. One of the largest benefits when using these systems commercially is the elimination of wasted water and nutrients, since the AQUAvalve feeds ONLY when needed, with no waste. Another nice benefit of these systems is that a multitude of growing mediums may be used including soil, coconut coir, perlite, rockwool cubes and fine gravel. Inset photo shows AQUAvalve.

Vertical Gardening

This is another interesting application of aeroponics. It was invented by Vertigro and represents a great way of saving greenhouse space. The system functions much in the same fashion as an aeroponic system except it shares a drain pipe with as many units as required. See the black hoses below growing cylinders. Vertigro provided the systems pictured here for Disney's Epcot Center in Florida. As you can see, hydroponic system design represents equal opportunity for a challenge and progress. If you can master the basic skills of plumbing, which can be picked up best by DOING, you can have lots of fun experimenting and improving upon the hydroponic systems in use today. In a later section of this book you will learn how to build your own hydroponic and aeroponic systems that employ these advanced techniques. Login to howtohydroponics.com/interactive/ to continue learning and enjoy preferred pricing on all that makes your garden grow.

This vertically oriented aeroponic system was photographed at Disney's Epcot Center in Orlando. The inventor, Vertigro Systems, came up with a novel way to save space in the greenhouse with this method.

Plant Nutrition

The composition of Earth's atmosphere

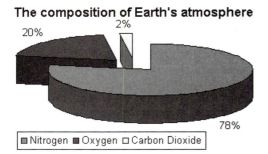

20%   2%

78%

■ Nitrogen ■ Oxygen □ Carbon Dioxide

Liquid nutrients have the advantage of being readily and evenly diluted when mixed into your reservoir. The high concentration of Iron chelates makes this graduated cylinder of Above & Beyond Vigor take on a yellow-orange appearance.

To develop a solid fundamental understanding of hydroponics, we must first review the organic composition of plants. And in order to do this, we must understand what elements are, and how they are used by living organisms for life processes. The molecule is the smallest recognizable assembly of atoms that can be identified as a specific element. Some common elements you have no doubt heard of include Hydrogen, Oxygen, Gold and Silver. All organic matter on Earth is comprised of at least four basic elements. In fact, the scientific qualification for labeling matter "organic" is that it must be comprised of the following elements: Carbon, Hydrogen, Oxygen and Nitrogen. Over 90% of a plant's dry weight is comprised of these four organic elements. The interesting thing is that while many claim plants grown hydroponically are not "organic," by definition, everything that grows is organic!

Plants live in the earth's atmosphere, which is comprised of approximately 78% Nitrogen, 20% Oxygen and 2% Carbon dioxide, in addition to a small percentage of inert gases. Carbon dioxide is known as a compound since it is a combination of one Carbon molecule and two Oxygen molecules. Most elements exist as compounds in nature because they are chemically unstable when pure in form. Most pure, unstable elements will react with other elements in nature until they are combined and stabilized into compounds. This is an important issue when choosing nutrients to use with your hydroponic system, so you should keep this in mind when you read about a single part nutrient that contains "everything" your plants need. By single part, I mean that it is all in one container. If this were the case, the nutrient inside would become useless in a very short amount of time because the elemental salts within would rapidly combine into compounds that plants simply cannot absorb. The compound H_2O (water) is made of two parts Hydrogen and one part Oxygen. H_2O is formed when Hydrogen, an unstable gas, is burned or oxidized (combined with Oxygen). Since C, H, and O are readily available in both the air and water, plants possess the ability to extract these elements from either and use them to create food using light as the catalyst.

The Organic Composition Of Plants

For a plant to develop properly, it must have access to all the necessary elements. Because these four elements occur naturally, most people rarely consider them when discussing plant nutrition. It should be stressed that the exclusion or depletion of any one of these elements would cause death of the organism. Just as you are what you eat, so are your plants, so feed them a well balanced diet.

(C) Carbon:
Occurs in the cell walls, in sugars manufactured by chlorophyll, as well as chlorophyll itself. Carbon constitutes approximately 50% of a plant's dry weight.

(H) Hydrogen:
Important in nutrient cation exchange (the chemical reaction which causes roots to uptake nutrients) and in plant-soil relations. Hydrogen is also essential for the formation of sugars and starches and is easily obtained from water. Water also keeps the plants structure rigid through what is known as turgor pressure, notice when a plant is lacking water it will begin to lose turgor pressure and wilt.

(O) Oxygen:
Required to form sugars, starches and cellulose. Oxygen is essential for the process of respiration which provides the energy plants utilize to grow.

(N) Nitrogen:
Necessary for the formation of amino acids, coenzymes and chlorophyll.

Macro Nutrients

Macro nutrients are those absorbed in large quantities from the growing media or in our case, the nutrient solution. They are the best known and recognized constituents of plant food and as such, are used as a handy guide in identifying the potency of a plant food. You may be familiar with these N-P-K ratings as printed on all commercially available plant food containers.

(N) Nitrogen:
Necessary for the formation of amino acids, co enzymes, and chlorophyll.
Deficiency: A lack of Nitrogen (in the form of nitrate and Ammonium) will result in spindly plants with small yellowish leaves. Some parts of the plant may turn purple.
Toxicity: Excess Nitrogen will result in overly vigorous growth, dark green leaves and delayed fruit ripening. Plants may also become more susceptible to pests.

(P) Phosphorus:
Prodction of sugars, phosphate and ATP (energy) - flower and fruit production - root growth.
Deficiency: Phosphorous deficiency causes plants to stunt and turn dark green. Lower leaves become yellow and may assume a purplish tinge as phosphorous is drawn from them to feed new growth. Leaves can curl backwards and droop while fruit production and the root system is compromised.

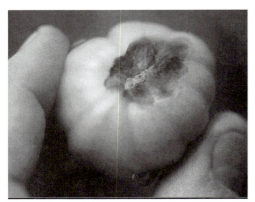

Blossom End Rot (BER) in tomatoes is caused by a lack of calcium to the maturing fruit. Often the cause of this problem is a sudden, intense heat wave which causes plants to transpire unusually fast and since Calcium is slow to travel through the plant, the result can be BER. Using shadecloth in the greenhouse during peak summer/sun is a great way to control heat and prevent BER in tomato crops.

Toxicity: Excessive Phosphorous will reduce the availability of copper and zinc.

(K) Potassium:

Protein synthesis requires high potassium levels. Hardiness, root growth, and the manufacture of sugar and starch also require potassium.
Deficiency: Growth slows while the older leaves develop mottling and plants becomes prone to fungus.
Toxicity: Excessive Potassium may cause a secondary Magnesium deficiency.

Micro Nutrients

Micro nutrients are those absorbed in small to minute quantities. They are generally less well known than the prev…souly listed Macro nutrients since most plant foods don't contain them. Here's the list of what they are and the effects they have on plants.

(Ca) Calcium:

Required for cell wall formation.
Deficiency: Calcium deficiency causes stunting and crinkling leaves. Young shoots die and blooms fall from the plant. Calcium deficient tomatoes will develop brown spots on the bottom of the fruit which will cause decay especially with the onset of high temperatures. This is called blossom end rot or BER.
Toxicity: Excessive Calcium is difficult to spot.

(S) Sulfur:

Protein synthesis, water uptake , fruiting and seeding, a natural fungicide.
Deficiency: Sulfur deficiency is uncommon but can cause young leaves to turn yellow with purple bases.
Toxicity: Excessive sulfur slows growth, leaves are smaller.

(Fe) Iron:

Chlorophyll formation, helps in respiration of sugars to provide growth energy.
Deficiency: Iron deficiency is common and causes new growth to become pale and blossoms to drop from the plant. Yellowing is initially observed between the veins and leaves may die along their margins.
Toxicity: Excessive Iron is difficult to spot and is quite rare.

This cucumber is suffering from several deficiencies as a result of being fed an inferior plant food product that lacked many of the micronutrients important to healthy plant growth. Most notable symptom here is lack of Iron (Fe)

(Mg) Magnesium:
Utilized in chlorophyll production and enzyme manufacture.
Deficiency: Magnesium deficiency causes older leaves to curl and yellow areas to appear between leaf veins. Only the newest growth will remain green as Magnesium is transported from the older leaves to feed the newer ones.
Toxicity: Excessive Magnesium symptoms are rare.

(B) Boron:
Necessary for the formation of cell walls in combination with calcium.
Deficiency: Boron deficiency results in brittle stems and poor growth. Stems may twist and split.
Toxicity: Excessive Boron will cause leaf tips to become yellow and die off.

(Mn) Manganese:
A catalyst in the growth process, formation of oxygen in photosynthesis.
Deficiency: Manganese deficiency causes yellowing of leaves between the veins and failed blooms.
Toxicity: Excessive Manganese can reduce the availability of Iron.

(Zn) Zinc:
Utilized in chlorophyll production, respiration and nitrogen metabolism.
Deficiency: Zinc deficiency results in small leaves with crinkled margins.
Toxicity: Excessive Zinc may also reduce the availability of Iron.

(Mo) Molybdenum:
Nitrogen metabolism and fixation.
Deficiency: Signs of deficiency are small, yellow leaves.
Toxicity: Excessive Molybdenum can cause tomato leaves to turn bright yellow in rare instances.

(Cu) Copper:
Activates enzymes, necessary for photosynthesis and respiration.
Deficiency: Copper deficiency causes pale, yellow-spotted leaves.
Toxicity: excessive Copper may reduce the availability of Iron.

(Co) Cobalt:
While Cobalt is not known to be directly required by plants, Nitrogen fixing organisms that help legumes like beans and alfalfa feed require Cobalt in trace amounts. Cobalt is also contained in vitamin B-12, which is vital to all forms of life, so there may be more to come on the subject as additional research is performed.
Deficiency: N/A
Toxicity: N/A

"If we really
are what we eat,
we best feed our
gardens well"

Indoor basil grow room - note the 6" PVC tubes - photo courtesy Sunlight Supplies, Vancouver, WA
Close-up shot of the author's favorite tomato strain which has an unusually high Brix, or 'sweetness"

Selecting A Hydroponic Nutrient

Most nutrients list the amounts of N-P-K represented in percentages. For instance, a 10-10-10 solution would contain 10% Nitrogen, 10% phosphorus, and 10% potassium by weight. If you do the math, you will see this concentration adds up to only 30%. That's because the remaining percentage of ingredients in the nutrient usually consists of other nutrients, filler or chelates used to assist the nutritional process. While you can use hydroponic nutrients for other methods of gardening, you can't use plant foods designed for soil gardening for hydroponics as these prodcts don't contain the proper balance of nutrients for this application. I personally favor the two and three part nutrient formulas because they always outperform the single part, general purpose formulas. The two and three part products allow you to custom blend your solution for each crop, and stage of growth for better performance.

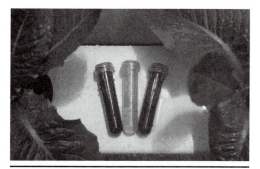

Hydroponic nutrients come in all flavors; powders and liquids, single part, two-part, three-part and then some. Choosing the best one for your application can by tricky, personally, I prefer a system that is simple to use, inexpensive to own and effective at growing a wide variety of crops to their fullest potential without requiring additional supplements or stimulants.

If we compare the measure of a plant's health to the strength of a chain, we find the plant is also only as strong as its weakest link. To insure that your "nutrient chain" is strong, it is very important to make sure all the links are in place, and in good supply. The proper concentration of nutrients within the solution is critical, as hydroponically grown plants are completely dependent upon what is mixed with water for food, and different plants have varying nutrient requirements. Many commercially available hydroponic nutrients now include instructions for mixing solutions specific to plant types, stages of growth and growing conditions. The wide selection of high quality commercially available products makes it easy to get started in hydroponics for those not looking to make their own nutrients.

When selecting a nutrient to use with your garden, there are a few things you need to look for. The most important factor is that the nutrient be designed SPECIFICALLY FOR HYDROPONIC applications. Using a common fertilizer like

Commercially available nutrients offer growers convenience, value and trade secrets that improve nutrient availability to plants over those which you may choose to make on your own.

While many may argue, I'm not a big fan of Organic Nutrients for use in hydroponic systems. The reason is simply that an "organic" nutrient is by nature not a "clean" nutrient and as a result, they generally do not dissolve well or stay in solution. (the picture above shows what was left in my test reservoir after only one month of use with an organic nutrient) Organic nutrients require the actions of bacteria to decompose the constituent material so unless there is an oxygen rich "home" for these bacteria within your system, the nutrients will not break down and will leave your plants undernourished. Metal salt hydroponic nutrients dissolve completely and stay in solution, making them available immediately and round the clock to your crop. My recommendation is to use Organic nutrients in the ground where they have available bacteria and time to decompose properly to become available to your plants.

"Magic Grow" is not advisable as these formulas are designed for use as a supplement to soil gardens and do not contain the micro and trace elements essential to the hydroponic environment. The second consideration in choosing a nutrient is that of using a powder or liquid formula. Multipurpose, single part powdered nutrients are o.k. for growing plants hydroponically under low to moderate lighting conditions but if you plan to grow under High Intensity Discharge lighting or in strong, direct sunlight, you will find using a two-part powdered or liquid nutrient gives you better performance. The reason for this is simple, one part, multipurpose nutrients are designed to satisfy the widest range of plants, lighting conditions and stages of growth. They are not custom-blendable according to your specific crop or conditions. I prefer the two and three part liquids for exactly this reason - you can blend them in different concentrations and combinations to target the specific growth requirements of your crops at each stage of growth. This is a very powerful technique in optimizing growth in your garden.

Making Your Own Nutrients

It has come to my attention over the years that there are many interested in making their own nutrients so I have provided a few recipes. If you are reading the Acrobat version, you will find a nutrient calculator spreadsheet included with your download. Otherwise, please consult the table on the next page which details the salts required to make three hydroponic nutrient solutions for use with vegetative, fruiting and flowering crops.

The weights shown in the following tables are based on making 1 gallon of stock nutrient solution. To make more than a gallon, multiply the gram weights by the total gallons of stock nutrient solution you require, for example, 2, 5, and so forth. These formulas have all been tested with a wide variety of plants in the same system, and have performed quite well. However, your results will depend upon the quality of raw materials and the precision with which you combine them. To mix your nutrient solution, fill an empty container with clean, warm water. Multiply the listed gram weights of each specific salt by however many gallons your container holds and dissolve each salt one at a time before adding the next. Once all salts are dissolved, allow the solution to cool before diluting it for production use in your reservoir. You will need an EC or TDS/PPM meter to determine

To make   **1.00**   **gallon(s) of**   **VEGETATIVE NUTRIENT**   **9.5 - 5.67 - 11.3**

Use	6.00	grams of	Calcium Nitrate	$Ca(NO_3)_2$
	2.09	grams of	Potassium Nitrate	KNO_3
	0.46	grams of	Sulfate of Potash	K_2SO_4
	1.39	grams of	Monopotassium Phosphate	KH_2PO_4
	2.42	grams of	Magnesium Sulfate	$MgSO_4 * 7H_2O$
	0.40	grams of	7% Fe Chelated Trace Elements	See Trace Box

To make   **1.00**   **gallon(s) of**   **FRUITING NUTRIENT**   **8.2 - 5.9 - 13.6**

Use	8.00	grams of	Calcium Nitrate	$Ca(NO_3)_2$
	2.80	grams of	Potassium Nitrate	KNO_3
	1.70	grams of	Sulfate of Potash	K_2SO_4
	1.39	grams of	Monopotassium Phosphate	KH_2PO_4
	2.40	grams of	Magnesium Sulfate	$MgSO_4 * 7H_2O$
	0.40	grams of	7% Fe Chelated Trace Elements	See Trace Box

To make   **1.00**   **gallon(s) of**   **FLOWERING NUTRIENT 5.5 - 7.97 - 18.4**

Use	4.10	grams of	Calcium Nitrate	$Ca(NO_3)_2$
	2.80	grams of	Potassium Nitrate	KNO_3
	0.46	grams of	Sulfate of Potash	K_2SO_4
	1.39	grams of	Monopotassium Phosphate	KH_2PO_4
	2.40	grams of	Magnesium Sulfate	$MgSO_4 * 7H_2O$
	0.40	grams of	7% Fe Chelated Trace Elements	See Trace Box

Chelated Trace Element Mix

Iron	Fe	7.00%	Copper	Cu	0.10%
Manganese	Mn	2.00%	Boron	B	1.30%
Zinc	Zn	0.40%	Molybdenum	Mo	0.06%

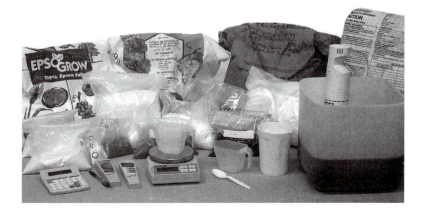

Note:
Refer to the labels on each of the elemental salts you purchase to familiarize yourself with safe handling practices. Store raw salts in a cool, dry place to keep them from absorbing moisture from the air which will offset their actual weights. Avoid using inaccurate "kitchen" type scales to weigh salts - accuracy, especially when making small batches, is critical.

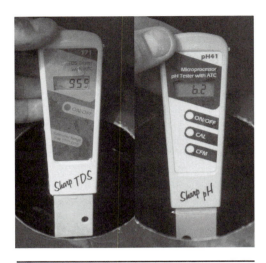

Meter on left shows a reading of 959 Parts Per Million, always take into consideration the starting concentration of your water and subtract that from your final reading to get the actual concentration of nutrients in solution. In this case, our water is 59 PPM before adding nutrients so our actual concentration is 900 PPM.   The meter on the right shows a pH of 6.2. It is best to adjust the pH of your water after adding nutrients and waiting a period of one to two hours for them to mix thoroughly.

This simple liquid pH test and control kit will enable you to maintain the pH of your nutrient solution inexpensively and with ease.

how much of these stock solutions you will need to dilute into each gallon of water in your reservoir..

Maintaining Nutrient Concentration And pH

For optimal growth to take place, the nutrient concentration and pH must be consistently balanced over time to insure plants have what they need, when they need it. In any circulating hydroponic system, with every pass the nutrient makes past the root system, an exchange is taking place. As a result, as time goes by, your nutrient solution changes in concentration. Therefore, so does each plant's ability to uptake essential elements. The easiest way to keep on top of your nutrient solution is to take a measurement of PPM or TDS (Parts Per Million and Total Dissolved Solids). This measurement is also commonly referred to as the EC or the "Electrical Conductivity" of a solution, because that is actually what you are measuring. There are a number of methods of measuring PPM. My favorite is the digital PPM meter that is submerged in the nutrient solution for a reading to be taken. Digital PPM meters are calibrated using a solution that has a known PPM value and you must calibrate them every so often. But nothing beats their convenience. Frequent nutrient solution changes will generally keep the concentration where it needs to be. My best advice is to carefully follow the directions that come with the nutrient you plan to use.

All the nutrients in the world will not do a plant any good if it cannot absorb them easily. A major factor in determining a plant's ability to uptake nutrients is the relative acidity, or pH (the negative log of the hydronium ion concentration) of the soil or solution from which they feed. pH is taken by measuring a voltage (potential) in a solution and registering it on a scale of 0-14 that represents the concentration of hydronium ions in solution. Generally, it is used to determine whether a solution is acidic or basic. If your pH reading registers a 1 on the scale, this represents a high hydronium ion concentration (an acid). Pure water is considered neutral at a pH of 7. A 14 on the scale represents the lowest concentration of hydronium ions (basic, alkaline). When adjusting pH, it is best to give your fresh nutrient mixture several hours to stabilize before attempting to adjust it. You should also be aware that commonly available pH control products are very powerful, and a little bit too much can sacrifice your entire nutrient solution fast. For first timers, I would even suggest mixing up a single gallon of nutrient solution, letting it sit for a day, and then counting how many DROPS of pH adjustment (up or down) it takes to get it to a range of 6.0 to 6.5. You can then multiply your count by the volume of your reservoir as a baseline for rapid, full reservoir adjustments. Some nutrients may become unavailable to the plant if the solution pH drifts from an optimal reading, which for most plants is between 6.0 and 6.5. This condition is called "nutrient lockout". pH can be tested with litmus paper and adjusted with an inexpensive pH control kit. Follow directions on product packaging.

Replacing your nutrient solution every 2 weeks is the best insurance against crop damage, as frequent changes will provide your crop with all the nutrients it needs. Under ideal conditions, pH and PPM will drift only slightly as the nutrient solution is used by the crop. Another great way to keep your nutrients in the "green" is by using a larger reservoir. The extra capacity acts as a buffer and maintains pH and concentration better than a reservoir that is "just big enough to do the job." It has been a long term goal of mine to discover and develop an automated system for managing the nutrient solution in the garden. After years of trials and tribulations with mechanical dosers and pumps, my good friend Edward Kim has engineered a solution with my help which should be available by the time you are reading this. To learn more about automating the task of nutrient mixing and delivery, and to check up on our progress, login to howtohydroponics.com/interactive/ and also enjoy preferred pricing on all that makes your garden grow.

Nutritional requirements vary throughout a plant's life cycle. In addition, light intensity, stage of growth (vegetative or flowering), and the general size of the plants you are growing all play a role in determining nutritional requirements. By regularly monitoring pH and PPM, you will have the ability to make corrections to your nutrient solution before your crop suffers. There are certain signs to look for when testing the PPM and pH of your nutrient solution. The following page outlines these signs for you.

An unusually high pH will decrease the availability of Iron, Manganese, Boron, Copper, Zinc and Phosphorous. A pH that is too low will reduce availability of Potassium, Sulphur, Calcium, Magnesium and Phosphorous. As a quick reference, the pH of common solutions are as follows;

Battery Acid = 1
Vinegar = 2.75
Orange juice = 4.25
Boric Acid = 5
Milk = 6.75
Pure Water = 7.0
Blood = 7.5
Sea Water = 7.75
Borax = 9.25
Ammonia = 11.25
Bleach = 12.5
Lye (caustic soda) = 13.5

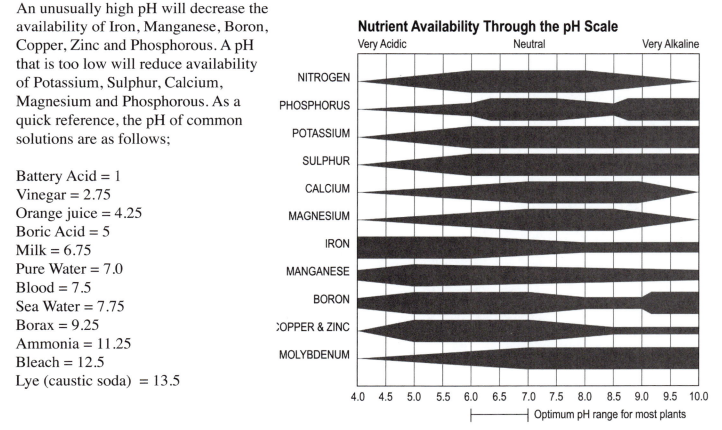

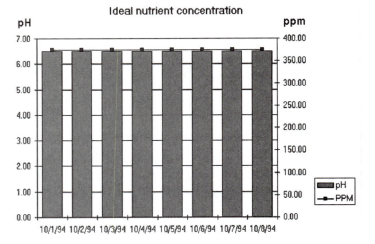

Ideal nutrient concentration

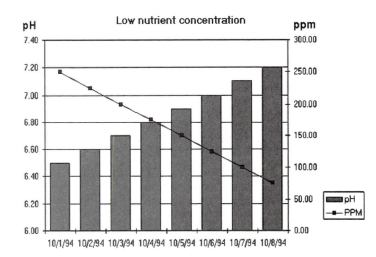

Low nutrient concentration

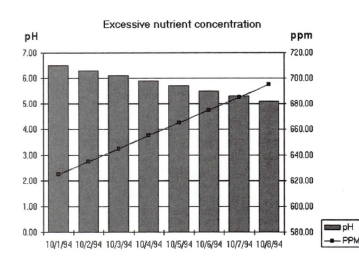

Excessive nutrient concentration

Since pH and PPM generally share an inversely proportional relationship, by measuring pH, you can sometimes infer what's happening to the concentration of your nutrient solution. These charts attempt to illustrate this principle.

Top chart:
In this example a perfect balance exists between plant requirements, solution pH and nutrient concentration. This is exemplified by steady readings in both PPM and pH over time. Naturally the volume of nutrient solution decreases over time, however, that is not indicated here... Your goal is to deliver exactly what the plant requires - no more - no less - temperature and light intensity play a major role in determining this balance.

Middle chart:
The crop is consuming more nutrient than water, note the PPM decrease. Since most nutrient solutions have a pH buffer which tends to pull down the pH, the decrease in concentration results in the rise of pH.

Note:
Many times what you may observe to be a nutrient deficiency i.e.: yellowing older leaves, red petioles and stems, may actually be caused by an excess of nutrient or unhappy pH - be sure to use that pH and PPM test kit and meter!

Bottom chart:
Here the plants leave excess nutrient behind. This imbalance causes PPM to increase, effectively decreasing pH, causing nutrient lockout. Possible causes are high heat/intense light which will increase the plant's transpiration of water as the plants "sweat". Diagnosis of these problems is important. Once you get into a routine with a particular crop and growing environment, you will develop a knack for what should and should not be, making this seemingly complex process simple. Keep a log and LEARN!

Nutrient Solution Microbiology

All bodies of water possess a dynamic balance of microbiological activity. In hydroponics, we strive to keep the nutrient solution as sterile as possible, but nonetheless, nutrient solution is by its very nature the perfect place for things to grow. Some microbes require dissolved oxygen to live (aerobic), and others do not (anaerobic). As a general rule of thumb, aerobic bacteria are "good," and anaerobic are "bad." Put simply, the by-products of anaerobic respiration are acids that wreak havoc with chemical and biological balances within the nutrient solution, which in turn harms the root system. Warm, stagnant water holds little dissolved oxygen, making it an ideal breeding ground for anaerobic bacteria, many of which (Fusarium, Pythium) cause crop failure as they take up home in the fragile root system and proliferate. The foul smells associated with warm stagnant water (sewers, swamps) is caused by these "bad" bacteria. Methane gas (swamp gas) is a highly flammable "natural" gas that is also a by-product of anaerobic bacteria. Can you see how, left unchecked, these bacteria can ruin a crop? Rampant pH swings, swampy smells, root rot and ultimately crop failure are the tell tale signs of a poorly balanced biology within your system.

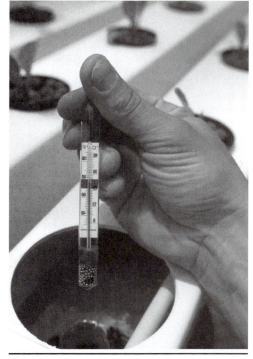

An inexpensive aquarium-type submersible thermometer is a great way to monitor the temperature of your nutrient solution in both the reservoir and growth chambers of recirculating hydroponic systems.

Combating this problem is simple, once you know its causes. First of all, warm water holds less dissolved oxygen than cool water, so keep your nutrient temperature between 68-75 degrees F. Secondly, keep the nutrient circulating so it's constantly picking up oxygen. Anywhere there is falling, spraying or rapidly moving water, you can assume dissolved oxygen is being added. If you have a large reservoir that circulates very slowly, adding a small aquarium pump can help supply extra oxygenation. I have found however, that aquarium airstones clog with salts after just a few weeks in a nutrient reservoir. A preferred method is to take a small bypass off the pump line to provide a bit of current within the reservoir. At the end of this bypass, I attach the end of the airline so the bubbles and nutrient flow distribute evenly throughout the reservoir. Last but not least, providing a "bacterial breeding ground" within your reservoir will help the good bacteria establish themselves and fend off the anaerobic invaders. A sponge or porous bag of horticultural perlite submerged in your reservoir will provide the perfect home for aerobic bacteria. Use 1/2 gal. of perlite in a stocking for every 25 gal. of reservoir.

Health Tips>	1. Nutrient temperature 68-75	Signs of imbalance listed below>>
	2. Avoid stagnation - circulate!	1. Swampy smell in reservoir and chambers
	3. Supplemental oxygenation	2. Slimy brown rotten roots
	4. Provide bacterial breeding ground	3. Plants show signs of stress

A typical CO2 setup includes (from right to left) a large tank, adjustable pressure reducing regulator and flow meter. CO2 is tricky to manage, as a result, it is generally not recommended for beginners although the rewards can be up to 40% more mass at harvest time according to recent studies.

> Download A Free CO2 Calculator

If you have Microsoft Excel, you can download a free CO2 calculator to assist in planning and implementing CO2 in your indoor garden from;

www.futuregarden.com/environmental/co2_calc.xls

Supercharge Your Garden With CO2

As your plants "breathe" CO2 and "exhale" O2, the balance of these two critical gases begins to shift. In nature, this exchange fits in perfectly as animals "breathe in" O2 and "exhale out" CO2. Of course, a perfect world this is not. Modern industry and the burning of fossil fuels has somewhat "unbalanced" this effect. However, in your greenhouse or grow room, you will need to help your plants breathe by supplying a constant exchange of fresh air, which by nature contains about 2% CO2. If you have already employed a thermostat and humidistat in combination with a vent fan, there is a good possibility that these two mechanisms will provide a good exchange of fresh air. However, if your fan is not operating frequently enough, you may be starving your plants of their most important atmospheric gas, CO2. Generally speaking, it is best to exchange the entire contents of your growing area about once an hour during daylight hours. To do this efficiently, you can use a fan that either runs continuously at a slow speed, or a fan that runs at high speed in short bursts. To determine the size of the fan that is necessary, simply multiply the length of your growing area by its height and then by its width. This number (use feet as a measurement unit) will be the Cubic Feet of your area. When buying a fan, you will notice that they are sold according to "Cubic Feet per Minute," or CFM ratings. What this means is the amount of air this particular fan will move in one minute. Therefore, if your greenhouse or growing room is 10 feet x 10 feet x 8 feet, that's a total of 800 Cubic Feet. You will need an 800 CFM fan to exchange the air in the entire greenhouse in one minute. That's a big fan and you certainly don't need to move it all out in just a minute's time. I would suggest using a 100 CFM fan and running it for 4 minutes every half hour. You can do this with a cycle timer.

CO$_2$ And You

These days, CO2 is best known as the "greenhouse gas" that traps the sun's heat in earth's atmosphere. It is responsible for global warming and a host of environmental changes that include altered weather patterns and rising tides. CO2 causes these problems by insulating the earth from heat loss and reflecting some of the sun's heating rays back onto the earth. From the previous information, you know that plants require CO2 to manufacture food within their leaves. Many of you may have also heard that adding CO2 to the growing environment can significantly increase the growth rates of most plants. This is

100% true. However, managing CO2 is tricky because of the factors preceding this topic. For example, if you are constantly exhausting the air from your greenhouse or grow room, how would you supply a never ending supply of CO2? You could add a CO2 cylinder with a regulator as shown on the previous page. The regulator can be set to slowly "leak" CO2 into the air flow of a reciprocating fan in order to evenly distribute it across the growing environment. You could hook the regulator up to an electrical valve called a "solenoid" which is then controlled by either a timer (timed to go on when the exhaust fans are off), or to release every X minutes for X minutes (another use for a cycle timer). You could hook the solenoid valve up to a CO2 measurement and delivery system that would deliver CO2 once the levels dropped below those you set as minimum. There are many crafty ways to add CO2 to your garden. The trick is to make it cost effective and safe. CO2 is not a gas you want to inhale in high concentrations. Plants will only benefit from so much before you wind up choking them with too much.

CO2 is measured much the same way as nutrient in solution, that is, PPM (Parts Per Million). Most gardens and crops will benefit significantly when the concentration of available CO2 is kept between 1000 and 1600 PPM. You will need a CO2 test kit or meter to accurately monitor this value. However, you can use the charts that come with CO2 injection systems to determine how to achieve these levels using their equipment. Without using an integrated measurement/injection system, you will need to determine the size of your room in cubic feet, and using this volume, ask the CO2 injection system manufacturer to specify the right setting along the lines of "set the regulator to "X" PSI and open the valve for "X" minutes every "X" minutes between exhaust cycles. Since every CO2 system is inherently different, you will have to rely on the manufacturers recommendations to insure accuracy and proper delivery of this growth boosting gas to your growing area. CO2 can also be generated by using propane and natural gas burners, since these gases result in the discharge of CO2 and water vapor when burned. Of course, keeping an open flame in any unsupervised area is dangerous, so these kinds of CO2 generation systems must be operated with caution according to the manufacturer's recommended operating procedures. The advantages to using a natural gas CO2 generator include lower operational costs and they can often double as heaters for colder area applications. If you are growing indoors, the heat generated by these units is usually a problem that neutralizes their effectiveness since, to exhaust the additional heat, you will also wind up exhausting the additional CO2. If you are a beginner, I strongly advise leaving CO2 until when you gain experience and have your garden completely under control. There are a number of excellent books on the use of CO2 for gardening.

Do-It-Yourself CO2

One of my readers informed me of a simple way to create and distribute CO2 indoors using a few inexpensive parts. You'll need a one gallon milk jug, a pound of sugar, enough water to dissolve the sugar, a packet of yeast, and some tubing. Begin by drilling a small tight hole in the cap of your one gallon jug, then pass a length of 1/4" air tubing through it just enough so that it hangs inside the bottle. The other end should be placed near your plants, preferably behind a fan that will evenly distribute the CO2 throughout your garden area. Fill your container with one pound of sugar, add warm water and stir until completely dissolved (make sure you leave an air space at the top of the container so the tubing doesn't go under water) Add the packet of yeast, replace the cap and stir. CO2 will be released gradually as the yeast begins to digest the sugar. Recharge your "CO2 Generator" with fresh water, sugar and yeast once per week. Login to howtohydroponics.com/interactive/ to continue learning and enjoy preferred pricing on all that makes your garden grow.

Let There Be Light

Two 1000W HPS lamps provide supplemental lighting for the hundreds of exotic orchids in this custom greenhouse. The lamps have integrated timers which turn on as the greenhouse falls into the shade cast by a nearby tree line. About a year after taking this photo, the author paid another visit and found two more lamps installed and nearly double the number of plants. I guess gardening kind of grows on you!

In nature, plants depend on the energy of the sun. Through a process called photosynthesis, sunlight is converted into sugars to provide fuel for the plant's growth. These sugars are utilized as needed in a process called respiration, and excess sugar is also stored for later use. Photosynthesis is made possible by chlorophyll, which is contained within the leaf cells. Chlorophyll gives vegetation its characteristic green color. Light is trapped by the chlorophyll, activating the process of photosynthesis. Inside the chlorophyll, light energy is combined with carbon dioxide and water to produce oxygen and sugar. The sugar is then oxidized (or metabolized) through the process of respiration, producing carbon dioxide, water, and energy for growth. Excess oxygen and water are transpired by the leaf into the air. Plant growth, therefore, is directly affected by the color, intensity and duration of the light the organism receives.

High Intensity Discharge (HID) Lighting

Nothing beats the Sun when it comes to growing, however, new types of High Intensity Discharge lighting have made growing indoors a viable alternative. Many of you are familiar with fluorescent "grow" lights designed to grow plants indoors. These products are fine for low-light plants where limited results are expected. But what if you want to achieve the ultimate growth potential of your favorite plants indoors? or, supplement sunlight in your greenhouse? Your answer is to use High Intensity Discharge lighting, or HID for short. These lighting systems consist of a lamp, reflector and power supply and are designed to provide the maximum output of photosynthetically active radiation (PAR) for the amount of power consumed. HID lighting systems can illuminate your garden with the right quality and quantity of light to make for impressive results. Horticultural HID lighting is used by the world's premier growers to provide many benefits simply unattainable with conventional fluorescent and incandescent lamps. HID lighting allows commercial growers to increase crop yields, bring crops to market on schedule and produce crops when out of season, making them even more valuable to the consumer market. HID lighting is so efficient and powerful that many indoor growers turn a healthy profit even after the initial investment and the monthly electric bills have been paid. Until recently, HID lighting for horticulture has been prohibitively expensive for everyday gardeners due to a limited market and the costs of production. But thanks to the ingenious new lighting products by manufacturers like Sunlight Supply and Hydrofarm, lighting costs have been reduced to the point where everyone can enjoy their benefits.

Intensity

Light intensity is commonly measured in power (watts) per square foot. For optimal photosynthesis to occur a general rule of thumb is 20-50 watts per square foot, with 20 being best for low-light plants and 50 best for light loving plants. Maintain 250W HID lamps 12-14" from plants, 400W lamps should be from 16-24" and 1000W lamps a minimum of 24" from plants unless your lamps are suspended by a circular or linear light mover in which case you may decrease the lamp to plant distance by 25-50%. To increase light effectiveness, paint your growing area with a semi-flat white paint sometimes referred to as an eggshell finish. The minimal gloss in this type of paint will provide maximum diffusion while still allowing you to wipe clean any smudges or stains that may appear in time. Other wall treatments include;

Mylar 90-95% reflective
Flat white paint 75-80% reflective
Gloss white paint 70-75% reflective
Yellow paint 65-70% reflective
Aluminum foil 60-65% reflective
Black <10% reflective.

Duration (Photoperiod):

Most plants grow best when exposed to 16-18 hrs of light per day. Additional hours of light during the day have not been found to increase growth by any significant amount. Plants that exhibit photoperiodism, the trait that causes day length to trigger flowering, should be exposed to 12-14 hours of light once flowering is desired. Total darkness is required during the darkness cycle for flowers and fruit to form correctly. Select a

This indoor aeroponic garden flourishes under the light emitted from a 400W Metal Halide lamp. Shown growing Sweet Basil, Thai Pepper, Sage, Fernleaf Dill and Lemon Balm.

When lighting an indoor garden it is of particular value to establish an evenly lit area. A portable light meter can be of great help in this regard.

On the left is a Metal Halide lamp, notice the white/blue hue. The lamp on the right is a High Pressure Sodium and exhibits a warmer, yellow/orange hue.

Tomatoes in the middle of winter made possible with the hydroponic method and a little artificial light. These six Matusalah variety tomato plants yielded 39 handball sized fruit, adding up to almost 8 pounds of tomatoes! Not bad for a spare closet! The plants were grown under a 400W MH lamp until they set their first truss of fruit. At that point, the lamp was changed to a high pressure sodium conversion and all growing tips were pruned to prevent the plants from outgrowing the space. I learned of this method (called STTP for Single Truss Tomato Production) at the Rutgers University website, however, in checking back recently, it seems to have been removed. Do a Google search for more info!

timer to control the duration of HID light. Some popular plants that are frequently grown indoors and exhibit "photoperiodism are Chrysanthemums, Poinsettias, Bromeliads, Pansies, Gibsofilia, Fuschi, Petunia, Gladiolia and Roses. These plants will flower when their photoperiod is 12hrs. of light and 12hrs. of darkness. Using indoor lights and a timer, you can force flower them during market peaks to increase yields and provide on-time delivery.

Color (Photosynthetic spectrum)

Photosynthesis is most pronounced in the red (600-680nm) and blue (380-480nm) wavelengths of light. Horticultural lighting, also know as High Intensity Discharge (HID) lighting is designed to cover these specific wavelengths, known as the PAR spectrum (photosynthetically active radiation). There are two types of HID lamps which emit different color spectrums. Metal Halide lamps emit a white/blue spectrum. MH lamps are best used as a primary light source (if no or little natural sunlight is available). This type of lamp promotes compact vegetative growth. There are also MH to HPS conversion bulbs available which allow you to provide MH light during vegetative growth and then switch over to the HPS for fruiting/flowering stages of growth. High pressure sodium lamps emit a yellow/orange spectrum. They are the best lamps available for secondary or supplementary lighting (used in conjunction with natural sunlight). This type of light promotes flowering/budding in plants. HPS lamps are ideal for greenhouses and commercial growing applications. The Son Agro and Hortilux HPS lamps add an additional 30% blue factor to their spectrum, making them a better choice than straight HPS lamps for solo use. There are also HPS to MH conversion bulbs available which can provide MH light during vegetative growth then let you switch back to HPS for the fruiting/flowering stages of growth.

White light Is actually a combination of all colors of light. Red + Green + Blue (and all colors in between)

Blue light stimulates hormones that trigger growth and inhibit dormancy. Blue light powers photosynthesis causing tips to grow towards the source (phototropism). Metal Halide lamps emit strong levels of blue light making them good for promoting the growth of leafy plants. Blue light also serves to keep plant growth compact and shapely by minimizing the distance between internodes (branches).

Green light is reflected, that is why plants appear green, however some green light is required for growth. HID lamps do not emit much green light, neither do high pressure sodium lamps. Red light also powers photosynthesis, aids in seed germination , helps to form pigments and aid flowering.

Red light is also responsible for triggering dormancy in some plants. High Pressure Sodium bulbs emit red light and are generally better for flowering and fruiting plants.

Far-Red light speeds up some full sun plants, reverses some red light effects. HID lighting usually doesn't emit far-red except in the case of some High and low pressure sodium bulbs, more so in the form of heat rather than photosynthetic light.

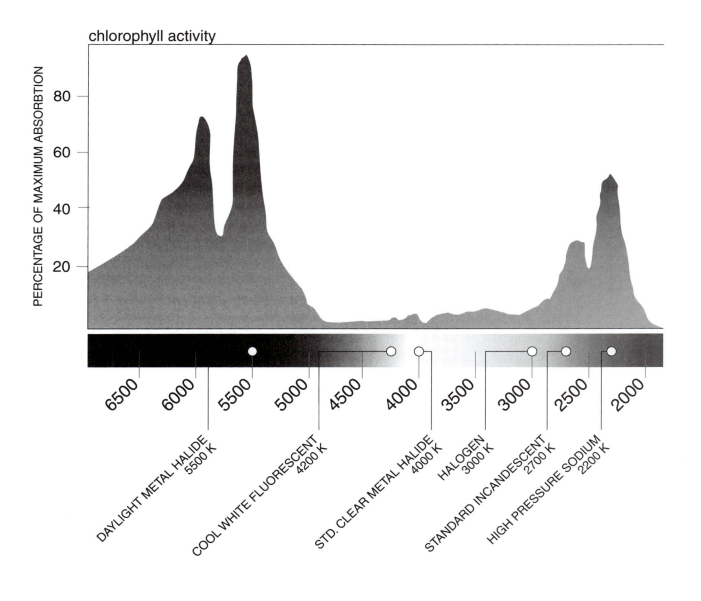

Anatomy of a grow light

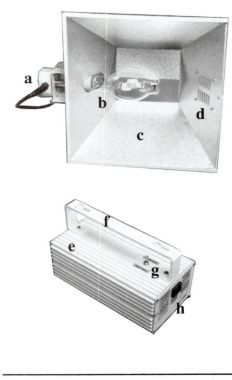

The lighting system shown above consists of a reflector which is usually suspended above the garden on a chain and pulley system for easy height adjustment and a ballast which is connected to the reflector with a cord through which it supplies the power. The purpose of the ballast is to step up and maintain line voltage.
a. Lamp cord and socket assembly.
b. Bulb (400W Metal Halide shown)
c. Reflector or "lamp hood" (note reflective lining)
d. Exhaust vent cover
e. Ballast box (400W Metal Halide shown)
f. Handle with mounting keyways
g. MH/HPS switch (available as an option on better 400 & 1000W lighting systems)
h. Lamp cord socket (cord not shown)

Choosing A Grow Light

In choosing an HID lighting system, red and blue are the two primary colors of light you'll need to be concerned with. Blue light is most pronounced during the spring and summer months when the sun is highest in the sky. It is responsible for keeping plant growth compact and shapely. Red light, such as when the sun is lower in the sky during the fall harvest months, is responsible for triggering reproduction in plants in the form of flowers and fruits. Metal Halide (MH) lamps emit primarily blue light making them ideal for the vegetative growth stage. High Pressure Sodium (HPS) lamps emit primarily red light which causes exaggerated flowering and fruiting during the plant reproductive stage. Thus, if you plan to grow mostly leafy crops such as lettuce and vegetative herbs, your best bet is an MH lighting system. If you want to grow flowering plants, then invest in a Son Agro or Hortilux HPS since it adds about 30% more to the blue spectrum than does a standard HPS.

Remember, lights emit heat which needs to be vented to keep indoor gardens within 65-80 degrees and 50-75% humidity. The primary benefit to employing a High Intensity Discharge (HID) horticultural lighting system is the control it gives you over your plants' growing environment. In many areas, once fall arrives the growing season is over, and if you're a hard-core gardener like me, you'll miss it dearly! Horticultural lighting systems allow us all to extend the growing season by providing our favorite plants with the light spectrum and intensity nearly equivalent to the sun. This is a great advantage for those of us who appreciate having a year-round supply of fresh flowers, veggies and herbs! HID lighting is also a great way to jump-start spring by starting your seedlings months ahead of last frost. Another great advantage of indoor horticultural lighting is your ability to control the length of daylight thus empowering you with the ability to force flower your favorite strain even when completely out of season. Vegetative growth photoperiods are from 16 to 18 hours/day. More than 18 hrs. is minimally advantageous and not worth the cost in electricity. Flowering photoperiods are usually between 10 and 14 hours per day. Remember, to grow perfect plants, the secret to the right light is Intensity, Duration and Color!

Login to howtohydroponics.com/interactive/ to continue learning and enjoy preferred pricing on all that makes your garden grow.

Hydroponics As A Business

Many people dream of a relaxing and stress free occupation such as gardening. Few, however, will actually venture forth and start a gardening business. If this is a dream of yours, I've provided some insight and experience in this chapter to help you make the decision and to get started off on the proper path to success.

Making A Market For Your Garden

Many gourmet restaurants and markets will purchase high quality hydroponic produce, provided it is available in good supply and available on a regular basis. If you are interested in making a profit from your garden, you should first investigate the local marketplace and determine just what it is that you should grow. Don't try to compete with everyone else. Identify a unique opportunity for a high profit plant by interviewing the owners and operators of local establishments. I have found that growing culinary herbs is the best way to make extra income from a garden in my local area, quality Basil seems to be the most requested by local merchants.. Of course there's always tomato and pepper plants that are staple foods, but both require significantly more space and considerably more time to harvest. Growing fresh cut flowers can also be very profitable. However, it is a harder market to penetrate, and flowers take longer to grow than herbs. The reason herbs are such a great product to produce and market is simple. The most popular culinary herbs are all leafy plants that will grow like wild in your hydroponic garden. Before getting started, you should contact your local county clerk's office to determine what legal requirements you'll need to meet to start your own business. So let's take a look at how we can get started in making a market for your garden.

Investigate Your Local Market

The most important thing you can do before planting a seed is to visit your local markets and do some informal research. Determine what they sell, and where the opportunity exists. Take a look at the fresh herb sections and see what they have available for their customers and how fresh it is. Nine times out of ten you will be amazed at how ragged their "fresh" herbs are! Have a look at the prices, and jot them down. Also, take notes of the quantities being sold in each package. Usually fresh herbs are sold by the "bunch," which in most cases is about as much as you could grab in your hand. Study the packaging and labels used for fresh produce. Once you get started, you will need to create a unique identity for your own business and products. Visit as many small markets as possible in your immediate area. Compile your information and organize it so you can determine what is selling, and for how much. On the next page is a list of what I have determined to be the best selling herbs, in order of importance. Assign a price to each from the research you have conducted.

Here's an excellent online pricing reference
http://www.ams.usda.gov/fv/mncs/fvwires.htm

The most popular culinary herbs:

Basil: Ocimum basilicum

Dill: Anethum graveolens

French Tarragon: Artemesia dracunculus

Mint: Mentha

Oregano: Origanum

Sweet Marjoram: Marjorana hortensis

French Sorrel: Rumex scutatus

Rosemary: Rosemary officinalis

Chive: Allium schoenoprasum

Parsley: Petroselinum crispum

Thyme: Thymus

Sage: Salvia officinalis

A few bunches of dill, oregano and sage as grown in our Aerospring aeroponic system.

Product Quality Considerations

Product quality is, by far, the most important consideration that will determine your business success. If you are growing hydroponically, you are already ahead of the game. However, you will certainly want to perfect your method before considering entering commercial markets. If you are totally new to hydroponics and gardening, take a few months developing your green thumb, because once you go commercial you will be counted upon to consistently deliver quality produce on time. Another important factor in your success is product packaging. After you have perfected your crop and production techniques, you should turn your concentration to packaging. You will certainly want to use a visually appealing package for your product. Most commercial product is packaged in screen printed plastic bags with colorful logos. Since you are just starting out, and probably cannot afford that added expense, try inexpensive yet attractive packaging methods such as using a clear zip lock type of plastic bag with an attractive self-adhesive label. It is also a good idea to use a hole punch to make a couple of "breathing" holes in your bags to maintain product freshness. Give an extremely fine misting with water before sealing the bags. Use a small kitchen scale to weigh your herbs to ensure uniformity from package to package. photo courtesy Five Star basil & spice.

Consistency in labeling, marketing and advertising will build a brand for your business and give a competitive advantage in the marketplace!

Many patrons of gourmet markets will identify with a wholesome looking label indicative of the origin of the produce. An excellent method of building and growing your business is to invest some time and money in creating a visually appealing label and "brand" name for your packaging. By creating your own brand, people will recognize your products and have a handy "name" to refer to when telling their friends how fresh and wonderful your produce is. Creating your own brand will also allow you to enter into larger markets because your following will already be familiar with the quality of your product and attribute it to your "brand." This is how the mega-brands are created, and although you might not be thinking in terms of nationwide branding and becoming a "mega-sized" operation, it is nice to know that your hard work is building your reputation, and at the same time, positioning your business for future growth.

King of the Italian eatery is the very common Sweet leaf Basil

Once you have a high quality sample product available, even if it is from your first round of crops, package a few bunches, apply your labels, and introduce yourself and your products. It's a great idea to bring a cooler along with you, packed with ice to keep your samples as fresh as possible. This way, when you introduce your local merchants to your products, they will be fresh and appealing. This is especially important if you live in a hot climate and you plan to spend the whole day on the road, visiting merchants. It is also a good idea to print up simple business cards that match the labeling on your products. Take advantage of the software available today that helps you design materials for starting a small business. There are literally hundreds of titles on the shelf that include templates and royalty free artwork you can use to get started. If you can afford it, a good graphic designer is an excellent investment in your future success. Remember to position yourself as a wholesome grower that only uses the finest nutrients, purest water and NO insecticides, fungicides or herbicides in the production of your herbs. This alone will help sway people to trying your brand.

Approaching Prospective Customers

Now that you have a great product, nice packaging, and an idea of what is important, here are some suggestions on what to do and say. Start off with the smallest store you can find (the smaller the better), since the chances that the person you

The infamous Habanero pepper - another excellent specialty spice used in Thai and Cajun cooking.

encounter will be an owner or manager. If they express a sincere interest, you can realistically supply a smaller operation a lot easier than a large market. Start small but always think big. You will want to speak to the owner or buyer, so identify who they are and then approach them by simply introducing yourself with your name and telling them that you would like just a moment of their time to discuss your gourmet produce. Make sure you always have a sample with you (freshly chilled from your cooler). By putting the product directly in front of the customer, you can let your product do most of the talking, especially if you are a little nervous at first. Explain how you grow in a pure environment that is completely free of chemical pesticides, herbicides and fungicides. Let them know your crop is so healthy because it is fed the finest hydroponic nutrients and purest water. Assure them that you are (most likely) "just down the road," and you can deliver frequently.

Once you have established contact, here's the most important part of your business presentation! If at all possible, open your package right there in front of them, and get them to sample the superior fresh scent and taste of your products! If you can only do one thing, get them to taste your product. That is the single most important factor that will determine your success as a grower. Of course, since your produce has been grown in a clean, efficient hydroponic system, they will be infused with more flavor than your field grown competitors. The produce buyer will most likely immediately recognize the difference in your premium quality product from the scent, texture and deep, intense taste. Remember, good products that keep their customers happily coming back for more will keep them ordering! After you have established the desire to carry your products, your goal with this first account is to get them to agree to showcase your herbs in their market. If they are unwilling to make an initial financial commitment to carrying your products, tell them you would love a chance to sell on consignment. You will need to be competitive with their current suppliers, but if your product is of significantly better quality, you have the competitive advantage. Assume that every reseller is looking to double their money, so if a bunch of basil sells for $3.99, you can assume they are paying about $1.50 per package. Since you are leaving your products on consignment, and your costs (due to the higher quality farming techniques you use) are considerably higher than those grown in the field, explain that upon sale of the produce that they pay you 50% of their selling price. Now remember, I recommended that you to start small so you can gain experience and confidence. Once they agree to give it a try, and you work out a delivery and payment schedule, you are now in business. The next step is to deliver on all of your promises.

Once you establish an account and you visit the store regularly to deliver new product, pay close attention to how your product is selling and determine which are the hot sellers. Obviously, you will want to concentrate on growing the hottest sellers. I can tell you from experience that Basil will most likely be your best seller and most profitable crop. However, each market differs, and you will have to learn on your own what to grow. Keep your resellers supplied with new products, since people will tend to buy produce that is visibly fresh and in abundant supply. If there is only one bundle left, they may have the preconception that it has been sitting on the shelf. On the other hand, once word gets out, your products may start disappearing faster than you can supply them. This is a good problem to have! The next step is to scale your business by expanding your production and signing on new resellers. Seeds are usually readily available, so finding good stock should not be a problem. Follow the direction on the seed packets for proper germination and growing techniques. Remember, the most valuable information on the subject of making a market for your garden is to visit your local markets and see what is selling. Talk to your local merchants and listen to what they will gladly tell you about their requirements. They are always interested in new suppliers with superior quality products to offer to their customers. Login to howtohydroponics.com/interactive/ to continue learning and enjoy preferred pricing on all that makes your garden grow.

Let's Get Growing!

We're almost ready and now for the moment we've all been waiting for! It's time to put your new knowledge to use and get started growing. In this chapter we will explore some of the more popular cultivars, and learn about their preferred growing environments. We'll also learn about starting from seed, and how to take and root cuttings. But before we get started, lets quickly recap a few more important plant requirements.

Temperature - The rate at which plants grow is controlled by the temperature of their environment. Usually as temperature rises, so does certain aspects of the plant's metabolism that may or may not be within optimal ranges either for genetic factors, or for other limiting factors as discussed below. In order to achieve the best growth, it is important to keep your garden within the temperature range your crop requires to avoid stress and prolonged maturation.

Humidity - The amount of water present in air is known as relative humidity. High levels of humidity prevent plants from transpiring water through their leaves, since the air is already full of water. High humidity can also prevent plants from cooling themselves through the same process of transpiration, and can hurt by providing the right climate for powdery mildew and botrytis to flourish.

Light - All light is not created equally, especially as far as plants are concerned. Light that falls within the range of color that stimulate photosynthesis is called PAR (Photosynthetically Active Radiation), and it's the only kind that will influence the growth rate of your crop. Many light meters don't measure PAR, which limits the meter's value in determining how fast your plants will grow. Even if they don't measure PAR, most meters are useful for determining if the lighting is even across your garden. PAR light is produced by the Sun, HPS, MH and now compact fluorescent lamps.

CO2 - In enclosed environments, the normal concentration of CO_2 (325-425 PPM) can rapidly be depleted, resulting in slowed growth due to the lack of photosynthesis taking place. Providing plenty of fresh air or supplemental CO_2 (in the range of 1000-1500 PPM) will keep chlorophyll activity constant and plants growing rapidly.

Dissolved Oxygen -Dissolved oxygen (DO) is the measure of available oxygen in your nutrient solution. Roots require oxygen to perform respiration, and will suffer if the proper amount of oxygen is not regularly available to them. Stagnant water in reservoirs and ponds must be agitated or oxygenated if plants are to be grown in them directly. A general rule of thumb is to maintain between 5 and 25 PPM of DO in solution that directly feeds and bathes plant roots. If the proper level of DO is not available to the plant, anaerobic respiration will result which will quickly cause the production of toxic levels of ethanol by the plants.

pH - The pH of a solution is the measure of the relative number of hydronium ions it contains. pH measurement ranges between 0 and 14, with a pH of 7 being neutral, 0 as extremely acidic, and 14 extremely alkaline (or basic). When the pH is neutral, there are equal numbers of hydrogen ions (H+) and hydroxide ions (OH-) in the solution to balance it out. A solution with a pH from 0 to 6.9 has a greater concentration of H+ ions that makes it acidic. A solution with a pH of 7.1 to 14 has a greater concentration of OH- ions and it is alkaline, or basic, as a result. The pH in a nutrient solution is critical because it controls the availability of elemental salts to the plant. At pH ranges outside of the norm, nutrient deficiencies may occur due to their unavailability to the plant.

Electrical Conductivity (EC) / Total Dissolved Solids (TDS)
Electrical conductivity (EC) is a measure of how well a solution conducts electricity. The higher the TDS, the more conductive the solution. Nutrient concentration in a reservoir can be measured this way. If plants pull more nutrients than water the EC will decrease. If plants pull more water or you lose water to evaporation, EC will increase. Since every nutrient has a different EC, the best way to use this measure of concentration is to follow the label recommendations for mixing, test the EC or TDS and then use this value as a baseline to compare and adjust your nutrient solution to over time.

Growers Guide To Popular Plants

The following table outlines the favorite conditions for these plants to thrive in your hydroponic garden. Adhere closely to these parameters and you will be happily surprised by the results. Always use a high quality hydroponic nutrient and maintain a healthy growing area by allowing plenty of light, air and moisture to reach your plants. Seed packets will contain more information on the particular strain you wish to grow.

IMPORTANT NOTE: The nutrient solution concentrations shown here (PPM/TDS) are a general rule of thumb only. If you grow with a commercially available nutrient solution, be sure to follow the manufacturer's recommendations for use with the crops you choose to grow. This is primarily due to the variance in electrical signatures between the components used in the many different commercial formulations.

Plant name	Lighting conditions	HID Lamp type	Favorable temp.	pH	PPM/TDS
African Violet	Bright but filtered	250/400/1000W HPS	warm	6.0-7.0	840-1050
Basil	high light.	250/400/1000W MH	warm	5.5-6.5	700-1120
Beans	high light.	400/1000W	warm	6	1400-2800
Broccoli	medium to high light.	400W	cool	6.0-6.8	1900-2450
Chilies - Capsicum	high light.	400/1000W MH	warm to hot	6	1260-1540
Cucumber	medium light.	1000W	hot	5.5-6.0	1100-1750
Eggplant	high light.	1000W	hot	6	1200-2450
Endive - Chicory - Radicchio	medium light.	400/1000W	cool	5.5	1100-1680
Lettuce	medium light.	250/400/1000W MH	cool	6.0-7.0	560-840
Marjoram	high light.	400/1000W	warm	6.9	1120-1400
Melon	high light.	400/1000W	hot	5.5-6.0	1400-1750
Mint	medium to high light.	250/400/1000W MH	warm	5.5-6.5	1400-1680
Orchid - Cattleya	bright (2000-3000 Fc) light.	400/1000W MH	Day 90 - Night 55F	7.0-7.5	300-500
Orchid - Cymbidium	bright shady light.	400/1000W MH	Day 80 - Night 60F	5.5-6.0	300-500
Orchid - Denrobium	1800-2500Fc of light.	400/1000W MH	Day 90 - Night 55F	7.0-7.5	300-500
Orchid - Oncidium	2000-6000Fc of light.	400/1000W MH	Day 85 - Night 60F	7.0-7.5	300-500
Orchid - Paphiopedilum	bright shady light.	400/1000W MH	Day 75 - Night 65F	7.0-7.5	300-500
Orchid - Phalaenopsis	bright shady light.	400/1000W MH	Day 85 - Night 65F	7.0-7.5	300-500
Oregano	high light.	250/400/1000W MH	warm	6.0-7.0	1120-1400

Parsley	high light.	250/400/1000W MH	warm	5.5-7.0	560-1260
Pea (Snow, Snap)	medium light.	400/1000W	cool	6.0-7.0	980-1260
Peppers - Chillies	bright shady light.	400/1000W MH	warm to hot	5.5-6.0	300-500
Roses	1000-3000fC	400/1000W HPS	warm	5.5-6.0	1050-1750
Sage	high light.	250/400/1000W MH	warm to hot	5.5-6.5	700-1120
Scallion - Green Onions	medium to high light.	250/400/1000W MH	warm to hot	6.0-7.0	980-1260
Spinach	medium light.	400/1000W	cool to warm	6.0-7.0	1260-1610
Squash - Pumpkins	high light.	400/1000W	hot	5.5-7.5	1260-1680
Strawberry	high light.	400/1000W HPS	warm	6	1260-1540
Thyme	high light.	400/1000W	warm	5.5-7.0	560-1120
Tomato	high light.	400/1000W HPS	hot	5.5-6.5	1400-3500
Watermelon	high light.	400/1000W	hot	5.8	1260-1680
Zucchini - Summer Squash	high light.	400/1000W	warm to hot	6	1260-1680.

Getting Started With Seeds

Most plants rely on the seed as the primary method of reproduction. The seed is formed inside the female flower after pollination by the male flower. All seeds begin as an egg within the carpel of a female flower. After male pollen is introduced to the female flower by wind or insects, the egg becomes an embryo and forms a hard coating around itself. When seed development finally stops, the seed is released and it is carried by wind, rain, bird or bug to its final resting place. If all conditions are right, it will become a new plant and repeat the growth cycle process. If you plan to grow indoors, you may need to "play bee" and manually pollinate your flowers for them to bear fruit or seed if they are not of the self-pollenating greenhouse variety. With peppers and tomatoes, I simply "tickle" the open flowers with a soft artist brush to spread the pollen from flower to flower.

To provide a friendly environment for your seeds and/or cuttings, I like to use a 10" x 10" or 10" x 20" growing flat. Keep the humidity high by using a 6" clear dome cover. A little ingenuity and some Tupperware and clear plastic wrap will work too. You'll also need to select a starting medium and a growing medium. The starting medium is what you will plant your seeds or cuttings in until they grow large enough to be "transplanted" into the system. You obviously have to transplant because your friendly seed development environment is too small for the mature plant. Usually, you will be starting your seedlings in a growing medium. I have had excellent results with Perfect Starts, rockwool starter cubes and loose coco coir as a starting medium.

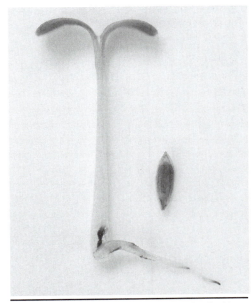

It still amazes me that such a tiny, benign looking object can sprout forth food for the planet and in return require only a little light and water.

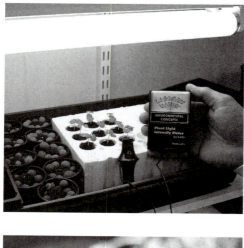

Tools of the trade - 10" x 20" flat w/ 6" clear humidity dome and electric heat to speed up the process of germination and rooting cuttings. Below, a simple light meter can help you evenly distribute illumination for optimal growth.

Vermiculite and perlite work well too, although I've heard there may be safety issues with vermiculite due to intermingled asbestos fibers.

The Perfect Starts sponges are made from organic compost that is molded into small plugs with a flexible binder maintains there sponge like texture and shape. This allows the hydroponic grower to use an organic medium for seeds and cuttings that can be transplanted directly into any type of system. The sponges protect the roots and keep the material from clogging spray heads. See the chapter on hydroponic mediums for more information. Avoid using soil to start your seeds because it is not sterile and may contain pests or pathogens that can infect your system. Water your starting medium with a 1/2 strength nutrient solution before use and keep it moist but not soaked while seeds or cuttings root. If you are using coco coir, it comes in dehydrated bricks that can be soaked in the 1/2 strength nutrient solution during the re-hydration process. See the chapter on growing mediums for more information on re-hydrating One brick usually makes about two gallons of loose coco coir, so you may not want to use the entire brick at once unless you have a lot of seeds to start.

Successful Seed Starting

From my experience working with many different means of starting seeds, I have developed a simple and reliable method for successful germination.

1. Pre-moisten starting medium w/ 1/2 strength nutrient, pH6.0
2. Maintain a root zone temperature of 72-80 degrees.
2. Maintain air temp. at 70-78 degrees and 70-90% humidity.
3. Soft light (20 watt/sq. ft.) until most sprout, then increase.
4. Feed 1/2 strength nutrient until light intensity is increased.
5. Discard weak and slow growing seedlings.
5. Move seedlings to production area once a second set of true leaves appears.

Seedling heat mats are an excellent way to speed germination, especially when you are growing out of season. They are also useful when cloning which is discussed on the following page. I have heard that presoaking seeds in a solution of water and 10% hydrogen peroxide can get them to germinate faster too. I've had some success with this trick, give it a try!

Making clones of your favorite plants

Another good method of starting and restocking your garden is cloning. While "cloning" may sound like a term for the five o'clock news, gardeners have been propagation identical plants for hundreds of years using this simple technique. To begin, a small "growing tip" is taken from a healthy specimen and is "planted" so it can grow its own roots. This method is independent of the plants reproductive system, and therefore eliminates any possibility that its "offspring" will continue to evolve. The cloning procedure results in plants that are identical in all aspects. Cloning is very popular with indoor growers wishing to preserve the characteristics of a particularly favorite strain. In order for cuttings to root properly, the following must be observed:

1. Root zone temperature 72-80 degrees.
2. Air temperature 70-78 degrees and 90-100% humidity.
3. Indirect, low intensity light (20 watt fluorescent).
4. Root feeding with dilute 25% strength nutrient solution .
5. Rooting hormones help cuttings root faster.
5. Foliar feed dilute 15% strength nutrient spray - optional.

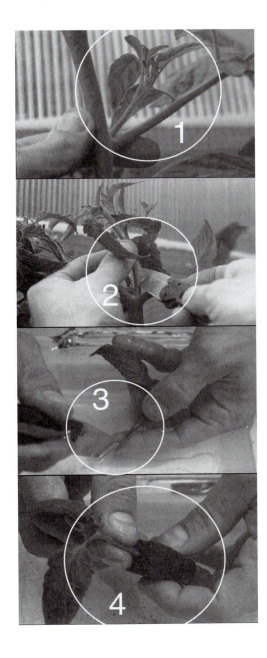

Procedure:

1. Select a healthy growing tip from a plant you wish to clone. The tip should be approximately 3" to 5" long, and include no more than two sets of leaves (including the tip). Always select fresh green growing tips for the healthiest cuttings.

2. Using a sterile knife or razor, sever the tip and immediately place into a room temperature bath of dilute nutrient solution or a prepared cloning solution such as Olivia's (see label instructions for more information).

3. Make a fresh cut while submerged at a 45 degree angle just above the last cut (end). This will assure that no air bubbles (embolism) are trapped in the stem which could impede the uptake of water and nutrients.

4. Dip the cut end into your choice of cloning gel or powder and quickly but gently insert the cutting about 1/2 to 3/4" into your choice of starting plug or medium. I used a Perfect Starts rooting sponge for this demonstration.

The cutting is now ready to be enclosed in a flat with humidity dome under a soft light source. Maintain a bottom temperature of 72-80 degrees Fahrenheit, humidity of 90-100% and soft lighting (20 watt fluorescent) until roots develop in 7-21 days. after which time your cuttings are ready to be transplanted to their final destination or to an intermediate area with stronger lighting where they can harden off before being exposed to a high intensity lamp or the sun.

Stocking Your Hydroponic System

Once your seedlings or clones have established a root system and have "hardened off," they can be transplanted into your system. If you used Perfect Starts or another plug or cube type starting medium, this process involves nothing more than placing them into your system and turning it on. If you used a loose starting medium like perlite or coco coir, you'll need to use a basket liner to keep the loose material from falling into your system and clogging it. I have experimented with aquarium filter cloth and have found that a fine layer of filter cloth between the coco coir and net cups seems to work well. There are now coir cup liners made from coco fibers as well. To transplant into the hydroponic planter systems described later in the book, dig a small hole in the LECA, place the new plants into the hole and gently fill in the LECA around the roots. To place your plants into net cups and try to get the roots as close to the bottom as possible. Fill in around the roots/sponge/cube with LECA to hold it in place.

When you first place the plants into your system, give them a few days of lower than normal lighting so that they can recover from the move and re-establish their vigorous growth. Keep a watchful eye on your new plants. If they look a little wilted, reduce the intensity of the lighting. It is also a good idea to water your plants from above with the nutrient solution for a few days. This will ensure that their roots are kept moist while they are adjusting to their new home. The picture at left shows salad greens and basil seedlings after they were transplanted to grow cups in preparation for placement in my PVC system. I usually keep them in the cups outside of the garden (as pictured) for about three days under soft fluorescent light and top water them before placing them into the system and under HID lights. If you are growing indoors under an HID light or if you are growing outdoors in the sunshine, it is a good idea to harden off your seedlings/rooted cuttings this way by placing them near a sunny window (but out of direct light), or by lifting your grow lamp to about twice its normal distance from the plants. Once they have two to four days of reduced light, you can gradually start increasing their exposure. Once their roots find your nutrient solution, watch out! They'll grow like crazy!

The Stages Of Growth

A plant's life cycle begins with germination, usually recognized by the above-ground appearance of a growing shoot. Mated to this shoot are two small, round leaves known as cotyledons (see photo at right). As these leaves begin manufacturing food, the plant enters its seedling stage of growth. During this time, the plant develops its first set of true leaves, resembling those of the mature plant and the primary formation of a root system begins. The root development that takes place at this time is key to the rate at which the plant will continue to grow. Providing the proper environment for the roots will ensure that your crop will have a chance to flourish. As I have said before, the main advantage of hydroponic systems is how they maintain optimal root health!

Once the root system can support further growth, the vegetative stage begins. Because growth during this period is primarily focused on stem, branch (also referred to as "frame") and foliage, plants need large amounts of nitrogen (N) that is required for the production of chlorophyll. The most substantial growth over the lifecycle of the plant occurs in the vegetative stage, and will continue unless interrupted by a change in the environment or lack of water and nutrients. The final stage of a plant's lifecycle is its reproductive stage. Because the plant's objective is now to reproduce and thus carry on evolution, most of its energies are devoted to the manufacture of flowers, seed, and fruit. The primary nutritional requirements begin to shift at this time from a high-N diet to a low N, high P-K diet (remember our discussion on macro-nutrients!). This is due to a considerable slowdown in vegetative growth while reproduction takes place. This change prompts the gardener to switch his or her nutrient solution from a vegetative formula to a flowering or "bloom" formula. Many hydroponic nutrients now come as a two-part system for exactly this reason. In some plants, reproduction is triggered by a change in the length of daylight, this characteristic is called photoperiodism. It is this characteristic which governs when these plants may be sown and harvested if growing outdoors. If you are growing indoors, be sure to provide the proper photoperiod for your crop or they may never fully develop. Changing the length of artificial daylight can trick the plant into flowering early. For example, commercial growers use this "trick" to deliver flowers to markets out of season, and at premium prices.

If you do plan to grow indoors you may have to play "bee" by pollinating the flowers on your plants manually since the insects that would normally do this in nature will not be there. For tomatoes and peppers, a delicate touch with a brush on each flower will help the plant pollinate itself to produce fruit. There are commercially available "plant shakers" that vibrate the flowering plants every so often to accomplish the same result. I have found that the breeze from a strong circulating fan is often sufficient to cause pollination indoors as well. If this sounds like too much work for you, choose a variety that is bred for the greenhouse as they will usually be of the self pollinating type and require no extraneous effort on the part of the grower. Login to howtohydroponics.com/interactive/ to continue learning and enjoy preferred pricing on all that makes your garden grow.

Problems In The Garden

As your garden's caretaker, keeping it healthy and happy should be your number one priority. Since it's a lot easier to prevent problems than it is to correct them, a problem prevention program that is based upon the information in this chapter will help insure your garden's ultimate success.

The First Line Of Defense

The first rule in keeping your garden healthy and happy is to keep it pest free. The simplest way to achieve this is to keep it clean and free from debris, especially when gardening indoors. Outdoor gardens are subject to the forces of nature like rain and wind that help to keep pests off your plants. Outdoors problem pests are also kept under control by natural insect predators, as well as birds and small animals. Since environmental conditions are not within the outdoor gardener's control, one must keep in mind that extended periods of rain, cool weather or extreme temperatures can weaken a plant's defenses and trigger an outbreak or infestation. If such conditions exist or become persistent, you may be forced to take steps to protect your plants from the environment until the inclement weather passes. If you live in a geographic area where such conditions are frequent and unpredictable, you may even want to consider investing in a climate controlled greenhouse.

When gardening indoors, many of the natural pest controls that exist outside are no longer available to your garden, so additional steps must be taken to prevent infestations, as well as the breakout of disease and fungi. Keeping the indoor garden clean should be your highest priority. Many pests find their way into the indoor garden on the soles of muddy feet and the fur of the family pet. You must be diligent in removing any and all debris, dust, dead or dying leaves, sickly plants and so forth. Look for anything that can act as a breeding ground for mold and mildew, or as potential food for insect larvae or maturing adults. While most plants have built-in natural defenses against disease and pests, they are only as strong as their overall health or vigor. Over or under feeding, excessive humidity, or lack of ventilation can all contribute to reducing the vigor of your garden and can open the door to disease and infestation.

Tools used around the garden should be cleaned with a 10% bleach solution after every use to prevent transferring disease causing pathogens. Never share tools between indoor and outdoor gardens, and make sure you store your outdoor and indoor tools in separate areas! Excessive humidity and condensation allow mold and mildew spores to flourish, so be sure to keep the air circulating quickly enough to remove excess humidity. When plants are grown too close together, moisture from transpiration can build up between leaves and provide the perfect breeding ground for molds and fungi. If you spill water (or nutrient solution) on the floor, clean it up immediately. Hard, smooth surfaces provide no cover for pests and allow the easy removal of mold and mildew. Avoid using carpets and cloth indoors, they are both excellent substrates for culturing fungi and harboring insect eggs and larvae. You may be tempted to "share" your indoor garden's

HID lights with potted plants. Don't. The healthy indoor hydroponic garden is a pristine soil free environment, and you'll need to keep it that way to avoid bringing problem after problem on yourself. Adopt the motto, "laboratory clean," and succeed!

Fungi, Algae And Disease

Excessive moisture in the air (humidity), on the leaf, and within growing media are the leading causes of fungi and mold outbreaks. Fungi are spread by spores that are carried aloft in the air. Spores are present all around us, and can be avoided only by using the strictest air quality standards. Unfortunately, maintaining this level of air quality standards is practical only in the laboratory with the use of expansive filters and air scrubbers. For gardeners, your first line of defense against fungi such as gray mold, powdery mildew, and damping off is to pay close attention to the following conditions that will readily allow spores to colonize.

1. Maintain low humidity - 60-80%
2. Insure proper ventilation - keep air in the garden moving!
3. Remove all dead and dying organic matter (leaf and stem)
4. Never over-water when growing with media!

Additional preventative measures can be taken to avoid fungi outbreaks. These measures include the use of powdered sulfur and copper; however, their use requires extreme caution because they can rapidly damage new growth if used excessively. If fungi become a persistent problem in your garden, even with preventative maintenance, you essentially have no choice but to employ a fungistat or fungicide.

Botrytis, or gray mold, is the most common fungi that plagues garden plants. It's a problem I know all too well. In July 2002, during a solid two weeks of rain, I lost an entire crop of cucumbers to this fungi. Although the humidistat in my greenhouse made sure the exhaust fans were running day and night, the moist cool air they were drawing in did little to keep moisture off the plants. Since it was the middle of July, I had my Dutch bucket system's watering cycles set for sunny skies and hot, dry air. With the sun blocked by clouds, and the air at nearly 100% humidity, transpiration slowed to a crawl and this unfortunate combination of events resulted in over-watering.

Grey mold more commonly know as Botrytis is shown here on this fallen cucumber stem. Its cause was a combination of over-watering and excessive humidity in the greenhouse.

Powdery Mildew flourishes in cool areas with high humidity, particularly after long periods of rain which make maintaining optimal humidity difficult. Sulfur pots are used in commercial greenhouses to fight this problem since the burning sulfur changes the pH on the leaf surface making it uninhabitable for molds and mildew

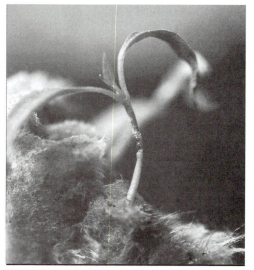

Excessive moisture in this rockwool cube led to the demise of several pepper seedlings as shown here suffering from damp-off.

Algae grows rampant when there is sufficient light and nutrients available in the water. Here a young Water Lilly is being choked by an algae bloom in a man made pond. Imagine what would happen if the pond was filled with nutrient solution! - Since we can't take the nutrients out of a hydroponic system, keep stray light from reaching the nutrient solution at all times.

Since Botrytis is present in the air at all times, the combination of these two conditions caused an explosive outbreak. It was a painful lesson to learn. So if you encounter similar conditions, keep this in mind. Fresh outbreaks of gray mold may be removed from plants with a dry, soft cloth. Be sure to remove all dead and dying plant matter from the garden as soon as you see it, because that is where Botrytis will flourish first.

"Damping off" is a problem caused by fungi that plagues seedlings and cuttings grown in unsterile, overly saturated media. It generally attacks the meristem just above the media, causing the plant to wilt and fall over. A wet-looking dark stem with a light powdery coating is the signature of damp off, as illustrated here. Use only sterile, fast draining growing mediums when starting seeds, and for additional protection, apply a light dusting of diatomaceous earth (horticultural DE) on and around the meristem.

While not a fungi per se, the infamous fungus gnat adores the same conditions and will wreak just as much havoc if left unchecked. Fungus gnats only become a problem where overly saturated growing media exists. While the adult gnat is nothing more than a nuisance, their larvae, which live beneath the surface, feast on young and tender roots. This situation can stunt growth, as well as open the door for disease and fungal outbreaks. When growing with a combination coir and perlite growing media in Dutch or AutoPot systems, a top dressing of an inch or two of LECA stone will keep the surface dry and unappealing to gnats and most fungi because the LECA will help wick excess moisture up and away from the surface. Using a layer of LECA stone as a top dressing also helps keep the lightweight mediums in the pots when growing outdoors where they are unprotected from the wind and rain and reduces evaporative losses due to intense lighting..

Algae will grow just about anywhere there is stagnant water, excessive surface moisture, and light. It will grow inside reservoirs and within growing chambers that allow stray light to enter. Since algae is a type of plant, it will consume nutrients and continue to grow if left unchecked. In a reservoir, it poses little more than a slimy nuisance. But when it is allowed to grow unchecked on submerged roots, it will compete for food and oxygen. Algae will also grow on the surface of saturated growing media and should alert the grower to take corrective action when it appears. Scrape excessive algae to remove it, and then determine and correct the cause of the excess surface moisture. As a general rule of thumb, it is a good idea to flush your hydroponic system between crops with a 10% bleach solution to prevent the build up of fungi and algae over time.

Problem Pests

Yuck. I hate bugs. Especially when they infest my indoor garden. I'd never had a problem with Whiteflies until I brought a pepper plant from outside into my indoor garden. What a mistake. I broke every rule of indoor gardening, and I paid the price. I guess we sometimes ignore warnings, even our own warnings to others, because we assume "it won't happen to me." I had inspected the pepper plant outdoors, and found it to be "apparently" free from critters. Well I think you've already figured out the lesson here: don't make assumptions or allow any exceptions to this rule. Keep your indoor garden free from outdoor invaders! Outside, the bugs that are most likely to infest your plants are generally controlled by their natural predators. Inside, you have no such luck, and without any natural enemies, Whiteflies and Spider Mites can rapidly get out of control. Whitefly larvae will molt and become annoying little pests inside of seven days. Once the Whitefly larvae molts and gains wings, it will immediately spread the infestation by laying eggs within just days, starting the whole process all over again. The eggs remain dormant for about ten days before hatching.

Prevention is everything, but what if, somehow, a pest invades your garden sanctum? To take care of infestations, you need to be aware of the biological control options. First of all, I do not advocate the use of pesticides, even pyrethrin, which is made from flower extract. They are all toxic, no matter what they are made from, and let's just say that pests build up a tolerance to them, which only helps breed stronger strains of pests. Biological control means simply that we limit the negative impact of a pest population by introducing predator insects. It may sound like adding fuel to the fire to introduce another insect to your garden, but the predator insect population is controlled by the amount of food available. For example, Whiteflies. So as the predator insects eat the enemy, their population naturally decreases as the food supply declines. A perfect solution if you ask me, nature at its finest!

(Top) A cucumber leaf appears to be suffering from a nutrient deficiency or toxicity when in fact the damage was caused by spider mites on the under side of the leaf. Never jump to conclusions without thorough investigation when diagnosing plant problems! (Middle) Mealybugs like this one lay eggs in a fluffy white excretion which is easy to spot. Mealybug predator beetles do a wonderful job of knocking down their populations and ridding your garden of them for good. (Bottom) Scale is sometimes mistaken for part of the plant whose juices it feeds on, not surprising!

White flies sucking sap from the bottom of this tomato leaf

White fly larvae shown on dried up leaf above, encarsia formosa (white fly predator wasps) shown protecting fruit below. Each of these small cards contain the wasp eggs. Encarsia wasps are extremely small and are not a nuisance like their larger counterparts.

Another good, nontoxic method, is to use sticky traps that attract flies and then keep them sticking around a little longer than they would prefer. You can make these with yellow or blue paint (any cheap quick-drying kind will do) yellow for whiteflies, blue for thrips, a few cardboard strips, and a large jar of Vaseline or petroleum jelly. Simply paint the strips, let them dry, and gob on the Vaseline, which sticks pests just as well as glue. Use a trap for every 2-4 sq. ft of garden area.

Problem pest	Predator solution	Qty/sq. ft.
Whitefly	Encarsia formosa	Use 1-2
Spider mite	Phytoseiulus persimilis	Use 1-2
Aphids	Lady bugs, Lacewings	Use 1-2

Integrated Pest Management Web Sites

The following is a brief listing of university and government **Web sites** on biological control and integrated pest management:

APHIS Plant Protection Centers
USDA Animal and Plant Health Service
http://www.aphis.usda.gov/

Cornell's Biological Control Home Page
Cornell University
http://www.nysaes.cornell.edu:80/ent/biocontrol/index.html

North Carolina's National IPM Network
(North Carolina State University)
http://ipm.ncsu.edu/

Purdue's Biological Control Laboratory
University of Purdue Cooperative Extension
http://www.entm.purdue.edu/

University of California IPM Home Page
University of California at Davis
http://www.ipm.ucdavis.edu/

Simple sticky cards like the one shown here (blue for thrips, yellow for whiteflies) allow the grower to keep small populations under control and determine at a glance how bad an infestation is.

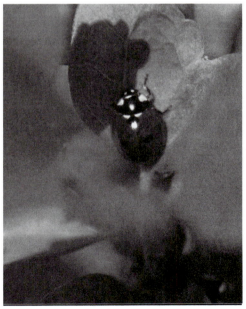

Ladybugs (above) and the Praying Mantis (top) are welcome sights in any garden since they have a voracious appetite for most garden pests!

If you are in the market for beneficial insects, check your local hydroponics retailer, garden center or Login to howtohydroponics.com/interactive/ to continue learning and enjoy preferred pricing on all that makes your garden grow..

Build Your Own Systems

Planning Your Hydroponic Garden

The first step in creating the right hydroponic garden for your needs is to create a plan. First, consider the space you have available for your intended garden. Don't forget that if you plan to grow indoors in a tight space, you will also need sufficient room to access your garden and to perform routine maintenance such as pruning and nutrient changes. For this purpose, leave yourself ample space to work. Don't try to fit too much garden in too small of a space. Remember, a hydroponic garden will give you a significantly higher yield than a soil garden of equal size. If you plan to grow indoors, you also need to consider access to direct sunlight. Most plants need a minimum of 4 to 6 hours of direct sunlight and a total of at least 12 to 14 hours of light each day. Most plants will not benefit from more than 18 hours of light a day. A south-facing window is a good place to start (assuming you live in the northern hemisphere). To provide supplemental lighting, or if your indoor garden location does not have access to direct sunlight, consider purchasing a High Intensity Discharge lighting system. See the HID lighting section of this book for everything you'll need to know to choose the right light for your needs.

If your garden will be located outdoors, you can take advantage of the natural sunlight. Make sure you consider the effects of the weather on your system, including the path of the sun and the temperature ranges for your area. Direct sunlight will heat up the nutrient solution in your garden, so make sure you consider this when locating the position of your garden's components. You'll want to maintain the nutrient temperature between 65 and 75 degrees for best results. Nutrient solution temperatures outside this range will slow the growth of your crop and can be detrimental as noted in the section on nutrient solution microbiology. Also note that if rainwater gets into your system, it will cause the pH and concentration of your nutrient solution to drift. So make provisions to keep rainwater out of your hydroponic system. Rainwater is more of a problem with the planter type of designs, such as the Dutch Bucket and the AutoPot, because they have a large exposed areas of growing medium to receive precipitation. You can minimize the rainwater problem by cutting skirts from plastic bags and placing them around the stems and over the grow sites. To protect the reservoir and nutrient solution from excessive heat and strong direct sunlight, consider using Celotex or another type of reflective insulation commonly available at building supply stores. Make sure all your electrical connections are kept dry, as per manufacturer's instructions. Note that most timers are not waterproof!

OK, we are almost ready to get started. Next, gather up the proper tools to make your job easy. A sharp razor knife, hacksaw and electric drill will make things easier, a 2 7/8" & 4" hole saw will be required to build the Aerospring and PVC gardens. While PVC is easy to cut with a hacksaw, cutting perfectly circular holes into the tubing is going to be next to impossible without this tool. If you don't own a heavy-duty 3/8" or 1/2" drive electric drill, you can most likely borrow or rent one. You will probably need to buy the 2

7/8" hole saw. Hole saws this size usually consist of two parts: an arbor that holds the drill bit (for drilling the pilot hole), and the actual hole saw, which looks somewhat like a half a food can with a saw-toothed edge. Note: Follow the directions on using this equipment before you pick it up, because this equipment can be dangerous without exercising proper care and precaution. If you don't own any power tools, or have experience using them, you may consider hiring an experienced handyman or carpenter to cut the holes for you. The best way I've found to cut these holes is to use a drill press and "shop clamps" to steady the pipes while cutting. But I've also built several 4" and 6" systems using nothing more than a 12V cordless drill and steady hand. So don't be discouraged, just plan it out in your head, take it slow, and just to be sure, measure everything twice, cut once!

Eight Hydroponic Systems You Can Build

Before we actually get started, there are a few more important considerations. The first is to decide the actual location for your garden. As we just learned, growing hydroponically outdoors is great because the sun is free and there's often plenty of space. But you may not be able to grow outdoors because you are in an apartment building or congested urban area. In this case, you have the option of growing indoors using High Intensity Discharge (HID) lighting. Whichever way you go, if you pay close attention to the guidelines discussed in this publication, you should succeed without difficulty.

If you want to grow indoors, plan on investing in an HID light. (see this book's lighting section for information on what kind of light will work best for your needs). I use a 400 watt metal halide lamp with reflective hood to light nearly four small gardens simultaneously, with excellent results. You may choose to substitute high output fluorescent instead, but you'll get more light output, and certainly more yield, with an HID lamp. In planning your light coverage for your new garden, try to get at least 30-40 watts of light per square foot of garden. I prefer 40 to 50 watts per square foot of garden, because I have found that the extra light makes a big difference. So plan ahead, and decide on your lamp sizes based on the growing area of each garden. If you want to illuminate more than one garden at a time, you can use this simple formula to determine your lighting requirements. Multiply your growing area's width by its length, and the resulting sum by 30 to 50 watts (depending on crop). The final number you get from this calculation is your required lighting wattage. Standard indoor HID grow lights come in 100, 150, 175, 250, 400, 600, 1000 and 1500 Watt sizes. Most high output fluorescents deliver about 10 watts per running foot of bulb. To achieve proper illumination with fluorescent lighting, plan on using an array of 4 bulbs for every foot your garden is wide. For example, if your garden will be 3' x 4' - use four 4' bulbs per foot of width, or twelve 4' bulbs total. This will give you 40 watts per square foot. Perfect! Keep them close to the plants too, no more than 6" to 12" maximum. Also remember, the combination of water and electricity can be hazardous to your health. Follow the safety precautions on product packaging and inserts. Keep your lights and ballasts away from moisture. And use a fan to circulate air throughout your garden.

When growing outdoors, your garden plan should include a way to protect the reservoir from heat and direct sunlight. Remember that you want to maintain your nutrient solution temperatures between 68 and 75 degrees F. If you are using a system that uses a pump to re-circulate the nutrient solution, consider burying the reservoir to take advantage of cool and consistent soil temperatures. You can also use aluminum foil to reflect sunlight to help prevent the reservoir from getting too hot. In hot climates, you can create a cooling loop and then bury it in the soil between the reservoir and the injector manifold to further dissipate heat. Note. this may require you to use a larger pump to overcome the extra resistance that the additional tubing will introduce. Indoors you can use a reservoir / water chiller to keep the heat down as well. Keep any electrical equipment protected from rain, and use only equipment that is stated to be suitable for outdoor use by the manufacturer. I also strongly recommend that you hire a licensed electrician to install the proper wiring and outlets to power your outdoor garden. Here are some additional factors to keep in mind when building your system. Hydroponic systems subject parts to a slightly acidic solution that can cause degradation of some materials. Avoid using metallic parts, especially for those that will come into contact with the nutrient solution. When choosing a reservoir, look for those made from resins approved by the FDA for use in constant contact with food. Rubbermaid Roughtotes are made from such plastics. Parts availability may require substituting an item here and there, so you may need to be crafty from time to time. Clean all parts before use with a 10% solution of bleach to remove mold release compounds and any contaminants they may have picked up while being stored. Avoid using automotive hoses and tubing, choosing only those made for hydroponics and aquarium use. And if you can't find what you are looking for at your local retailer or garden center, Login to howtohydroponics.com/interactive/ to continue learning and enjoy preferred pricing on all that makes your garden grow.

. The next few chapters detail the construction of eight different types of hydroponic and aeroponic systems. The following is a quick overview of each with important considerations.

Hydroponic System Plans Quicklist

1. The Hydroponic Planter
The simplest and quickest project to complete. Perfect for school, science fairs and windowsill gardening. Ideal for growing lettuces and small herbs, flowers and ornamentals. Not recommended for outdoor use.

2. The Lettuce Raft System
Another system that can be assembled in an hour or two, however, slightly more difficult to create due to the Styrofoam "raft" which must be cut from a sheet using a jigsaw. Excellent for indoor use by a sunny window or under a grow lamp. Best suited for growing lettuces and other short stature plants, hence the name. May be used outdoors however rainwater will dilute the nutrient and can cause an overflow.

3. The Aerospring Aeroponic System
The most popular design which has been carried over and improved upon from the third edition. This system requires a little more skill and experience with power tools. Suitable for indoor and outdoor use and for growing any type of plant from lettuce to tomatoes. No Redwood or palm trees please! Be sure to support taller, heavy plants with trellis or vine lines. Use with a 250W-400W grow light indoors.

4. The Dutch Bucket System and Aeroponic Fogger Option
An extremely versatile system suitable for growing anything, just about anywhere. It utilizes a growing medium which helps to make it a bit more user friendly than the pure water hydroponic systems described above and below. Excellent for tomatos, peppers, cukes, watermelons, just about anything can be grown, including root crops like onions and carrots. It's length makes use with a grow light tricky unless you use a light mover - consider modifying the design to make it more of a rectangular or square shape if you plan to grow indoors under a light. New with this release is an option to adapt this system to utilize an aeroponic fog - note - very experimental at this point in time!

5. The PVC Pipe Gardens
4" - Best for use with short stature crops and those that will mature quickly. Significantly less expensive to build than the 5" and 6" counterparts but an incredible performer as well.
5" - Best design in my opinion. The square chambers are attractive, stable and provide a healthy internal are for roots to develop.
6" - If you can't find the 5" PVC material or you prefer the round chambers, the 6" PVC system was the first and probably most successful and popular hydroponic system I've ever come across. You really can't go wrong with any of these systems but be advised they are more difficult to build than any of the other systems detailed for construction in this book.

The Hydroponic Planter

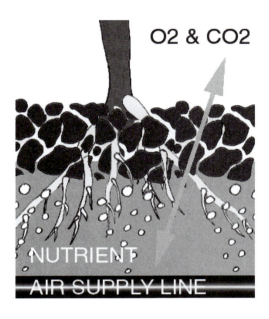

O2 & CO2

This is by far the simplest hydroponic garden you can construct in this book. It's made from a common plastic deck planter, some LECA and an aquarium air pump, air stone and tubing. The diagram at right details how the roots grow down through the LECA into the nutrient solution which is kept aerated by the air pump. Due to its open top design, it's better suited for use indoors as rainwater can cause it to overflow and dilute the nutrient solution at the same time. A 150-250W HID lamp will provide plenty of light for this little hydroponic garden to flourish.

NUTRIENT
AIR SUPPLY LINE

Parts List

(1) Plastic deck planter with sealed bottom. We used a Dynamic Designs 27" x 12" x 10" deck planter but you can use a round or square one as well by improvising. Make sure your container is free from holes and made of opaque (non-transparent) plastic.

(1) 2500cc minimum air pump. I used a single output pump with a "T" fitting to split the air tubing into two feeds. You can use a double outlet pump for better performance without the "T" fitting.

(2) 12" Air Curtains or (1) 24" air curtain to provide a stream of air bubbles to oxygenate nutrient bath - Needs to run the entire length of the planter.

(1) 1/4" Airline "T" fitting to split the output of a single outlet air pump - not necessary if using a dual outlet air pump or if you use a single air curtain that runs the entire length of the planter.

(1) 1/4" Air Tubing to connect pump outlet(s) to air curtain.

(28 ltr.) LECA or 3/8" gravel. This is to fill the Dynamic Design planter, others will vary. Make sure the medium is rinsed clean from grit and dust before use.

+ Hydroponic nutrients
+ Assorted rubber bands and plastic zip-ties

Tools You'll Need

A pen or marker
Razor knife for cutting tubing
Electric or battery powered drill w/ 1/4" bit (optional)

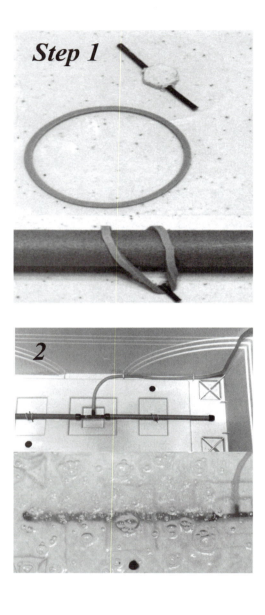

Step 1. If you are utilizing a non-weighted air curtains as in this photograph, you should secure it/them to the bottom of your hydroponic planter so they do not move around. I took advantage of small tabs molded into the bottom of the Dynamic Design planter to hold the air curtains down using some stainless steel wire and rubber bands. Make sure you don't use anything that will rust inside the planter. Of course you can also just pour the LECA right on top of the air curtain once it's plumbed as the weight will keep them in place just fine.

Step 2. The layout is real simple... Using the "t" fitting as shown, connect both air curtains to the supply line and route it along the bottom and up the side of the planter. You may also use a single air curtain of 24" or so in length and feed it from just one end. I drilled holes in some tabs that were molded into the planter to secure the airline. The LECA will hold the airline in place as well if there are no tabs available. After securing the air curtain(s) and attaching the supply lines, fill your system with water and run the pump to check for even distribution of air bubbles and absence of leaks!

If your system is bubbling away like this one, you can drain the water and continue on to the next step. If you do not have a steady stream of bubbles, make sure your air line is not kinked or clogged. If all else fails, try using a more powerful air pump. Always remember to keep the air pump HIGHER than the top of the planter to avoid it siphoning nutrient solution from the planter.

Step 3. You may choose to install a nutrient level indicator. To do so, simply drill a 1/4" or so hole through the bottom of a section of 1/2" clear rigid tubing as shown at left. This will allow you to secure the bottom of the tube to one of the tabs on the bottom of the planter using a plastic zip tie.

I highly recommend adding this feature since there is no other means of determining the nutrient level inside your planter.

Step 4. Attach the bottom of the level indicator to a tab through which you drilled another equal size hole - using a plastic zip-tie. We chose the Dynamic Design deck planter because of the many molded in tabs which allow easy connection to the planter.

Step 5. To make the level indicator float - simply cut a piece of 1/16 inch balsa wood into a large "match stick" shape so that it can easily side up and down inside the indicator tube. Now all you have to do is glue on a small piece of Styrofoam to add buoyancy. Either way, apply a coat of clear wood sealer to the stick to keep it from getting waterlogged. You can use a plastic drinking straw in place of the balsa wood stick if you can find one long enough. Try your local convenience store as sometimes they have extra-long straws for their Super-Sized fountain drinks.

Step 6. If you do in fact use a float - insert it into the tube and cut it flush with the top of the indicator tube.

Step 7. Now you are ready to fill your garden with freshly rinsed LECA or clean, pea-sized gravel. Fill it up to within two inches of the top. Fill the system with nutrient solution according to the directions that came with your nutrients. Try to add one gallon at a time and mark off the level on the dipstick as it rises up with the nutrient solution so you will have a reference to the nutrient level.

To insert your plants, simply dig a hole in the LECA as deep as the seedlings roots have grown and carefully backfill the aggregate around them. Make sure you get their roots down deep enough so they are getting wet. Water from above for a few days till they adjust. Once your seedlings or rooted cuttings have been planted, turn on the air pump and watch your plants grow!

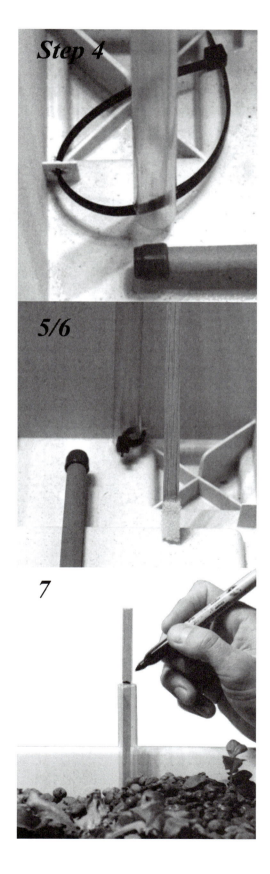

Step 4

5/6

7

The Lettuce Raft System

Each day I respond to more and more emails from people looking for the simplest, most inexpensive means of growing hydroponically. I often recommend the Hydroponic Planter from the previous chapter, however, this "simple and inexpensive" method just isn't complicated enough. So... after giving it some careful thought, a worthwhile solution presented itself. The raft system is simple, inexpensive ($20-$30 complete) and "complex" enough to satisfy any first timer's appetite for a fun project that actually works quite well. In concept, the raft system does exactly as it says. Plants are grown in Styrofoam "rafts" that float in a shallow pool of nutrient. To keep the nutrient from stagnating, a small air pump is used to deliver oxygen to the solution and eagerly awaiting roots.

Parts List

(1) 14 Gallon Roughtote reservoir
(1) Single outlet air pump
(1) 2' x 2' x 1.5" rigid foam sheet
(9) 2" net cups
(1) 6' x 1/4" air tubing
(1) Air stone
(1) Small bag of LECA
(9) Perfect Starts or equivalent seed starting/rooting plugs
(1) 1/4" compression grommet
+ Hydroponic nutrients

Tools You'll Need

Electric or battery powered drill - 3/8" or 1/2" chuck
1 7/8" hole saws for cutting plant sites
3/8"drill bit for drilling grommet hole
Jigsaw or coping saw for cutting foam
Razor knife for cutting tubing
A pen or marker

Author's first prototype raft system made from a plastic garbage pail. Plants shown were grown under a 95W 6500K fluorescent bulb which is said to provide similar output to HID systems yet without as much heat. Not bad for three week old lettuce.

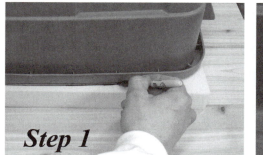

Step 1

2

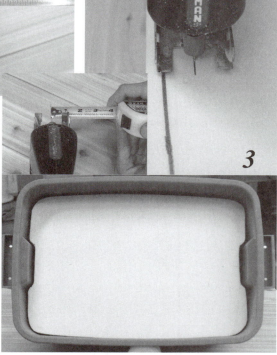

3

Step 1. Trace the outline of your container onto the styrofoam sheet as shown here.

Step 2. Measure the distance between the outer edge of your container and the inner wall (measurement 'X')

Step 3. Be sure to cut the styrofoam 'X' inches smaller than your outline so that it fits neatly inside the container. After a little bit of additional trimming, you should have a perfect fitting "raft" as shown here. Make sure it can move freely up and down inside the reservoir with it full of water since the pressure may deform it a bit. If this is the case, simply trim away until you can get from 4-8" of up and down movement. This is very important for this system to work properly.

Step 4. Layout the grow sites on your styrofoam raft and use a hole saw to cut them out. If you don't have access to a hole saw, you may be able to use a utility razor to perform the same task albeit more challenging!

4

Step 5. Mark off the lowest point your raft will reach inside the container (due to the wall taper or internal obstruction) so that you'll know when to top it off in order to prevent the nutrient level from dropping away from the bottom of the raft and leaving your plants high and dry.

5

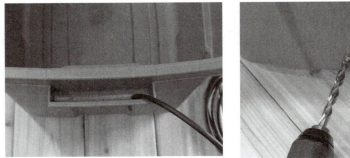

Step 6

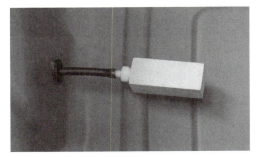

Step 6. Drill a 3/8" hole in the bottom wall of your container and insert the 1/4" rubber compression grommet. Pass your air tubing through the grommet and attach to your air stone.

WARNING! YOU MUST mount your air pump higher than the maximum water level in your container to prevent back flow of nutrient solution through the air tubing and into the pump.

Step 7. Time to plant your favorite seeds! I used a scissor to trim the bottoms off the Perfect Start #2's since they were just a bit too long for the little 2" cups I used here. Use LECA stones to back fill around the seeded plugs and place them into each of the grow sites in your raft.

Step 8. Fill 'er up! Add water, nutrients and plug in your pump, your raft garden will start gurgling and your plants will grow in no time - don't forget to give them plenty of light and top off the nutrient solution every time it drops 2-4" or so. It's also a good idea to completely flush and clean your raft system every other harvest using a 10% bleach solution and scrub brush.

The Aerospring System

If you have a hard time finding any of these parts, check the Futuregarden website for a complete inventory and assortment of parts and all-inclusive starter kits: www.futuregarden.com

Since the first edition of How To Hydroponics in 1994, the Aerospring design has been by far the most popular. Its low cost, combined with ultra-high performance, allows just about anyone to build a fully functional aeroponic garden for a fraction of what the commercial units cost. The Aerospring is fun to build and even more fun to operate. If you are looking for the best performance for the least investment, build an Aerospring!

Parts List

(1) 31 gallon Rubbermaid Roughtote reservoir
(1) 400 GPH submersible pump or similar
(5) 360 degree pin nozzle or 360 degree micro-sprayers
(2) 15" x 3/4" PVC spray bars
(1) 3/4" PVC 'T' FPT fitting
(1) 3/4" PVC endcap
(1) 3/4" MPT barbed adapter
(1) 3/4" Male Garden Hose adapter
(1) 3/4" Garden Hose cap
(1) 1/2" I.D. rubber grommet for sealing level tube exit
(1) 1/2" barbed elbow fitting for level tube assembly
(1) 1/2" rachet clamp for securing level tube on elbow fitting
16" of 1/2" blue tubing for level tube & 16" of 3/4" tubing for pump line
(1) 5/8" in-line filter for keeping sprayers clear
10' of 1/2" closed cell foam gasket tape for sealing lid
(1) Quart of LECA stone 8-16mm
(6) 3" net cups - FYI - You can use up to (8) cups per unit, 2 rows of 4 each.
(6) Perfect Starts or equivalent seed starting/rooting plugs

Tools You'll Need

Electric or battery powered drill - 3/8" or 1/2" chuck
2 7/8" & 4" hole saws for cutting plant sites and service port holes
3/4", 7/8" & 15/16" speed bore bits (flat, inexpensive drill bits)
1/8" drill bit if micro sprayers are used or 7/16" bit if pin sprayers are used.
Hacksaw for cutting PVC pipe
Razor knife for cutting poly tubing

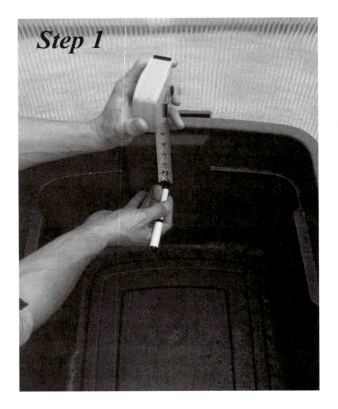

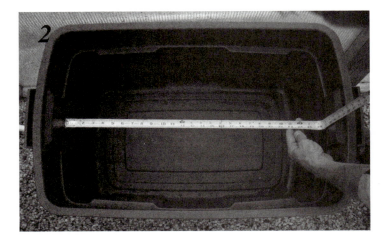

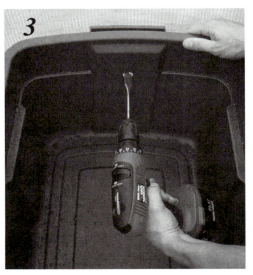

Step 1. Measure and mark off the locations where you will drill two opposing 15/16" holes that will hold the 3/4" PVC spray bar in place. With the 31 gallon Roughtote reservoir, mark the center of each hole 5" from the top if using pin sprayers or 4" from the top if using micro sprayers. Be sure to center the holes as shown.

Step 2. Measure the inside width of your reservoir, divide it by 2 and cut (2) pieces of 3/4" PVC pipe to this length. These will serve as your spray bars. Adding the 'T' fitting between them will give them the extra length required to exit either end of the reservoir and accept an endcap on one end and a garden hose adapter on the other.

Step 3. Using a 15/16" speed bore bit, cut out the two holes you just marked in the previous step. We purposely drill this hole smaller than the external diameter of the 3/4" PVC pipe so its a force fit, preventing any leakage.

Step 4. Using a 7/8" speed bore bit, cut a hole on one side of the reservoir bottom for the level tube grommet. This hole should be centered exactly 1" off the bottom - see inset photo.

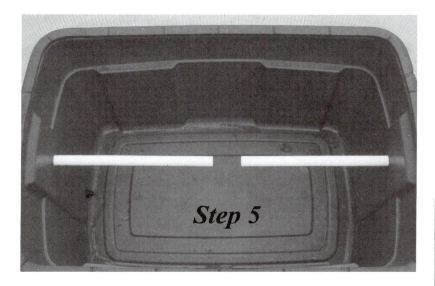

Step 5

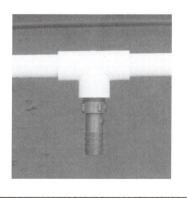

Step 5. Install the two spray bars you made in the last step by gently forcing their ends into the support holes as shown here. Press fit the 3/4" PVC 'T' fitting and screw in the barbed adapter as shown in the inset photo. I prefer not to use PVC cement on this junction to facilitate easy disassembly and storage.

Step 6. Affix the weather stripping foam tape to the reservoir to seal the lid from leaking. Be sure not to stretch the tape any or it will shrink back to size and pull free from the reservoir. This seal is very important and could leak if not done with care. Take your time and DON'T STRETCH THE TAPE!

Step 7. This photo was taken before I realized the 3/4" MHT adapter (black threaded nipple) can also be glued directly onto 3/4" PVC pipe. You can still build it as it is pictured in the photo, but the two extra parts pictured are unnecessary. The nice thing about this design is, you can use the pump to drain your reservoir by simply removing the 3/4" MHT cap as shown in my hand. Note that MHT stands for Male Hose Thread and it fits standard garden hoses to make draining simple.

Step 8. There are actually a few small steps to finish up here. a) Using PVC cement, glue the 3/4" endcap onto the other spray bar end - see picture. b) Insert the 1/2" rubber grommet into the 7/8" hole you drilled earlier. c) Gently press the 1/2" barbed elbow fitting through this grommet - you may want to use a little soap as a lubricant here. A snug fit is a must to prevent leaks. d) Cut a 16" piece of blue or green 1/2" tubing and attach to the elbow at bottom. e) Drill a 3/4" hole in the handle to secure the top of the level tube. You can keep the tube from pulling free with a plastic tie or clamp inside the handle.

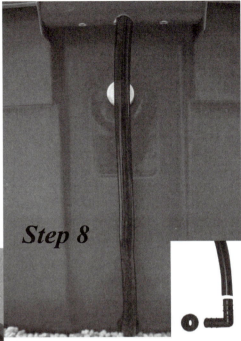

Step 8

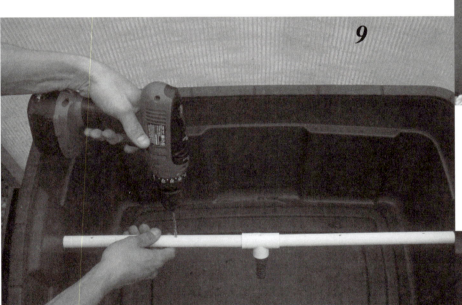

9

Note. Choose a sprayer that works at low enough pressure and delivers an even, 360 degree spray pattern. My favorites are the 360 micro sprayers and pin sprayers.

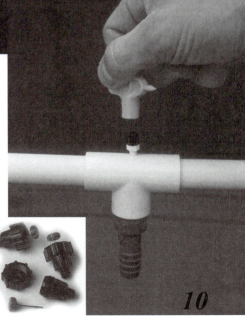

10

Step 9. (5) sprayers per unit seems to be the magic number here, although depending on the size of your reservoir and pump, you may opt otherwise. To use the micro sprayers shown, drill (5) 1/8" holes, equally spaced with one in the center of the PVC 'T' as shown in

Step 10. You will need a 10-32 tap to create the threads in each of these holes that allow these sprayers to screw in and out. The 360 degree pin sprayers (inset photo) come with a rubber seat that seals them into a 7/16" hole and make installation a bit easier. They both work very well and are easy to clean although the pin sprayers are slightly more expensive but you only need 3-4 pcs.

Step 11. After installing your sprayers, it's time to plumb the pump assembly. A few things to remember here are; a) Keep the pump tubing from kinking. b) Make sure the filter flow indicator arrow is pointing away from the pump. c) Use a hair dryer to soften the tubing and get it over the pump nozzle. You should use a stainless steel hose clamp on this junction which is not shown in the picture. Time has shown that the filter isn't really necessary - you're call!

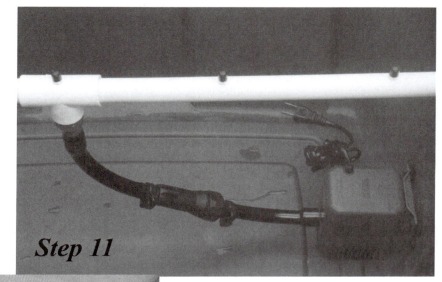

Step 11

12

Step 12. Fill 'er up with water and take it for a test ride. Adjust the rotation of your spray bars so the spray is as flat as possible. Never run your Aerospring dry - the top of the pump is the lowest level you should ever allow your nutrient to reach, any lower can cause pump failure.

Step 13. Time to cut out the plant sites and access port using your 2 7/8" and 4" hole saws (respectively). My favorite configuration is shown in this picture, use it as a guide to help you measure and layout your grow sites. Don't be afraid to add more grow sites as the nice thing about this design is that you can elect to have as many as your container will fit. Using 2" cups you can have up to 40 grow sites in this very same lid, an ideal configuration for rooting many cuttings all at once.

Note. It's a good idea to add the 4" access port on the same side as your pump. This will allow easy access to the filter, which should be inspected and cleaned every 2 weeks.

13

Aerospring Growers Guide

Aeroponic basil, from seedling to skyscraper in 45 days - here's all you need to know...

1. Start your seedlings or cuttings in a Perfect Start sponge, rockwool or oasis root cube. Place into a 3" net cup and backfill with LECA stones to provide physical support.

2. Fill your Aerospring with 10-15 gallons of water, add your choice of nutrients according to directions on label (do not use regular plant food - it must be for hydroponic use!) This is where the 4" access port comes in handy!

3. Using an intermittent cycle timer such as the NFT-1 or ART-2 will help keep your nutrient cool and save electricity since an aeroponic system must be run 24/7 to avoid drying out the roots.

4. Keep your nutrient as close to 70 degrees as possible. Warmer temperatures promote the growth of anaerobic bacteria which could harm your plants as they take up residence in the roots. Notice how white the roots below appear due to a healthy diet and massive oxygenation they receive when grown aeroponically.

5. Drain and replace your nutrient once it drops to the top of your pump. Use the discarded nutrient to feed your outdoor garden and landscaping - waste nothing!

6. Use a pH control kit to monitor and keep pH between 5.8 and 6.2 for optimal nutrient availability.

7. Use a 10% bleach and water solution to thoroughly clean the inside of your reservoir between crops, rinse afterwards.

8. Use a trellis to support tall plants as they do not have the soil to anchor themselves like in-ground plants.

The Dutch Bucket System

The Dutch bucket can be used with just about any growing medium. Shown here from left to right is coco-coir, LECA stone and perlite.

This simple to construct stand system allows you to expand your dutch bucket garden easily.

Staggered 12 bucket system shown here with two 36 gallon in-ground reservoirs.

This design is brand new for the fourth edition. After two years of research and experience in the greenhouse, I've developed a novel way to build a great garden with Dutch buckets. Since the buckets are mass produced, we'll focus on how to build the integrated drain stand and manifold that makes growing with them easy, and storing them off season even easier.

Parts List

(1) 31 gallon Rubbermaid Roughtote reservoir or your choice (shorter is better)
(6) Dutch Buckets - either black or beige will do
(1) 400 GPH submersible pump or similar
(1) 3/4 in. PVC w/ 1/2 in. FPT side-out (see picture)
(1) 6 ft. 1/2" ID plastic poly pipe
(2) 1/2" barb to MPT adapters (Male Pipe Thread)
The following parts are all 1 1/2" PVC pipe, cut and drilled as noted;
(3) 36" drain rails with 7/8" holes drilled @ 5", 18" and 31" from end.
(1) 10 1/4" top rail with 7/8" holes drilled @ 5" from end.
(1) 22 3/4" top rail with 7/8" holes drilled @ 5" and 18" from end.
(1) 5" drain spout
(3) 15" front legs
(3) 16 1/2" back legs
(3) 8" pieces for 'feet'
(6) 3" pieces for 'toes'
(9) 1 1/2 In. PVC Slip 'T' fittings
(4) 1 1/2 In. PVC Slip 'L' fittings
(6) 1 1/2 In. PVC endcap fittings
(1) Ultrapeat coco-coir brick for every 4 Dutch buckets
(8) Dry quarts of Aerolite horticultural perlite for every 4 Dutch buckets

Tools You'll Need

Electric or battery powered drill - 3/8" or 1/2" chuck
2" & 4" hole saws for cutting drain rail plugs and access port in reservoir lid
7/8" speed bore bit (flat, inexpensive drill bits)
Hacksaw for cutting PVC pipe and a razor knife for cutting poly tubing

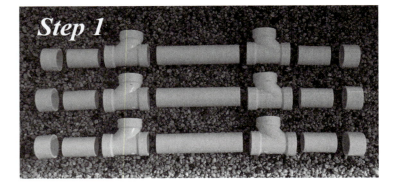

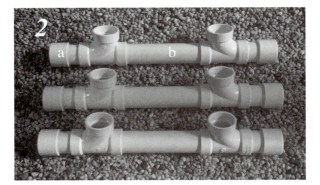

Step 1. Cut pieces for the 'toes'-(a) and 'feet'-(b) from your 1 1/2" PVC pipe according to the measurements given on parts list. Line up pieces as shown and test fit for accuracy before gluing.

Step 2. Glue these pieces together making sure the 'T' fittings line up perfectly and point in the same direction. Use a flat gluing surface or your stand will come out crooked.

Step 3. You can adjust the height of the legs to compensate for shorter or taller reservoirs. The sizes given in the parts list work perfectly with the reservoir we chose. As a rule of thumb, the front legs will always be 1 1/2" shorter than the rear legs since the Dutch buckets have a 1 1/2" recess in their backs for the drain pipe to fit into.

Step 4. Glue the legs into the bottoms making sure to use one long leg and one short leg for each stand - test fit before gluing to prevent the chance of overlooking this important detail.

   Note: While PVC glue dries very quickly, it is a good idea to allow it overnight to harden before putting any weight on the stand. A good rule of thumb is when the smell is gone, the glue is dry since the smell is actually the very solvent that keeps PVC glue in liquid form.

Step 5. Layout the drain and top rails that have been cut and drilled according to the parts list. Here, the two uppermost pipes make up the 6' drain rail. To prevent returned nutrient from filling the stands, you need to plug up the two 'L' fittings on either end and the single 'T' fitting that holds the two sections together in the middle of the 6' span (labeled a,b,c.) The drain spout (d.) should remain free and clear.

Step 6. To create the drain rail plugs, I used a 2" hole saw and cut them from a scrap sheet of 1/8" PVC plastic. I then glued them in as shown here using PVC cement and filled the pilot hole left by the hole saw with some PVC saw dust and glue. You can use silicone adhesive as well if you like, just make it leakproof at any cost.

Step 7. Assemble your drain stand as shown here. It is a good idea to dry fit the parts before you glue them together and keep in mind that gravity will hold the drain and top rails on the stand legs. If you don't glue the rails down, you can disassemble the stand easily and stow it away in the off season.

Note. Use a hard, flat surface to glue the rails together or they will come out crooked. Pay special attention to these photographs to determine the correct orientation of the parts

Step 8. Now that your stand is complete, you can put the Dutch Buckets into place by fitting the drain nipples into each of the 1" holes in the drain rail.

Step 9. Place your reservoir underneath the drain spout and mark off where the spout touches the lid. Here you will need to cut a 2" hole into the lid to accept the drain spout. Cut the 4" access port hole in an easy to access area of the lid as well. Plumb the pump and filter as shown here.

Step 10. Layout the manifold parts as shown here. There are a few different ways to create this same piece of apparatus using PVC parts. The bottom line is that it serves the right purpose. The screw cap on the MHT adapter allows quick draining.

Step 11. Now you can attach the 6' tubing to the feed manifold as shown and zip-tie the entire apparatus to the back side of the drain rail.

To seal the opposite end of the feed line, simply fold it over itself twice and secure with a plastic zip tie (See inset photo below) Alternately, you may elect to use a 1/2" barbed plug (not shown)

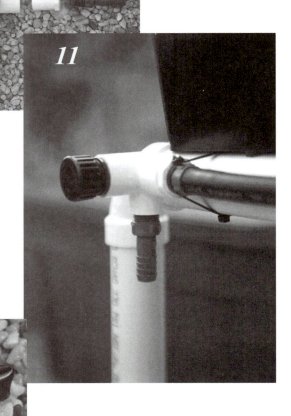

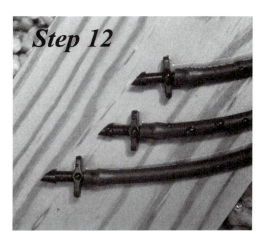

Step 12. You will need two drippers/emitters per bucket to insure even irrigation. Cut the drip lines from 1/4" tubing being careful to leave plenty of extra length for ease of use and maintenance. Drip lines are connected to the feed manifold using .16" barbed joiners as shown here.

Step 13. You will need a small, sharp punch to prepare the feed manifold for connection to the drippers. It is important that these holes are not too large or they will leak around the base of the joiners. Aquarium silicone applied to the junction (dry thoroughly first!) will stop most leaks.

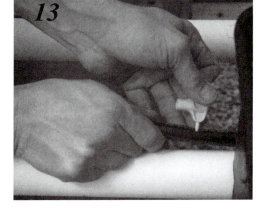

Step 14. Emitters are easily connected to the drip lines and inserted into your growing media. Most emitters are adjustable - space them evenly to promote even distribution of nutrient solution across the media surface and root mass below.

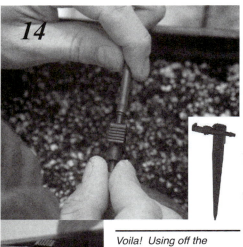

Voila! Using off the shelf micro-irrigation parts you've just created an extremely versatile hydroponic system.

A Cool Idea!

In order to maintain an optimal nutrient temperature for this custom greenhouse installation, the 46 gallon rainwater barrel reservoir was buried almost to its lid. This grower also chose to use 1/2" PVC pipe as the feed manifold material and threaded barbs which screw into holes tapped in the PVC for a leak-free connection.

The Dutch Bucket Garden Growers Guide

Growing medium

As a simple rule of thumb, a medium that holds a lot of water offers more protection against pump failure than one that holds little. The drawback is a "wet" medium has little room for fresh air and is a good breading ground for fungus and disease. If you have the luxury of an adjustable cycle timer and can check up on your plants frequently, I prefer to use a 60% perlite/40% coco-coir mix and adjust my timer so that the medium never gets soaking wet but never dries out completely. This setting is completely based upon the plants you grow, their size, ambient temperature and intensity of the sun. With all these variables, checking your garden every day or two is a very good idea this way you can make adjustments before problems arise. If you prefer to run your pumps constantly, choosing a medium like gravel or LECA stones will suit your needs as both of these mediums allow plenty of interstitial space for air to keep your roots happy.

Planting

Start your seeds or cuttings in your preference of starter cubes or sponges. Transplant once roots are clearly visible from the bottom of the cubes and plants are ready for your growing environment. It's a good idea to place the drippers close to the plants until they have a chance to develop some root, at which time (2 weeks) you can move the drippers closer to the edges of the bucket for better distribution.

Nutrition

Depending on your crop and stage of growth, you will want to choose a good quality hydroponic nutrient. Do not use fertilizers designed for soil gardening as they do not contain a complete balance of nutrients required for growing this way.

Feeding cycle

The feeding cycle has a lot to do with the medium you choose to grow with and even more to do with the environmental variables discussed above. Keep the medium moist, never wet and never let it dry out completely!

Maintenance

Drain and replace nutrient in reservoir when it falls to a level just above the top of your pump. Never let your pump run dry. Inspect and clean in-line filters with every nutrient change.

Storage

Drain reservoir and use to feed your landscaping or lawn. If using LECA stone or gravel, dump into a storage container and rinse thoroughly and allow to dry. Clean all empty buckets with hot water and allow to dry before packing away like this >

The Dutch Bucket Fogger

Roots grown in a nebulized fog respond by creating root hairs which exponentially increase their ability to uptake water and nutrients.

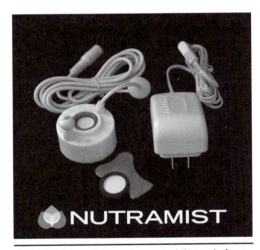

A single ultrasonic transducer module made from corrosion free PolyPropylene (PP) is required to generate the correct droplet size and volume of fog. The Aloxite coated transducer discs help facilitate easy removal of mineral buildup. The Cyclone mk4 shown below incorporates four modules in a ready to use machine for creating humidity, foliar feeding, aeroponics & pest control

Every now and then a new idea comes to mind, sometimes spurred by something I've seen here or there, but nonetheless something I feel I've got to share with you. Recently there have been some products appearing that utilize an ultrasonically induced aeroponic nutrient fog to feed plants. It's funny because my first experiment with hydroponics was one using a humidifier that worked on a similar principal. I will never forget the roots it produced! If you look at the close-up of the air roots I was able to coax from a sunflower, you will immediately notice the fine root hairs which due to their expanded surface area, allows them to absorb incredible amounts of Oxygen, food and water. Think plant metabolism on overdrive! Experimenters with this technology should take note that in an aeroponic fog system, if the spray goes away, your roots and crop will turn to hay. By using the Dutch Buckets for this project, you are afforded a little bit of crop insurance as the buckets do hold about a quart of water at the bottom before draining back to the reservoir. This will help ONLY if the roots are already reaching the bottom of your buckets. I've also experimented with adding some LECA Stone and/or Ultra Coarse Aerolite to the bottom of the buckets to hold a little water as the fog percolates up through the bucket bottoms.

By starting with the plans for the Dutch Bucket Garden in the previous chapter, we can make double use of its drain manifold by pumping the fog from the reservoir through it as well as a pathway for excess condensate to flow back to the reservoir.

PLEASE NOTE. Contrary to the other systems outlined in this book, the Dutch Bucket Fogger is 100% experimental which means if you build it, plan to spend extra time and money perfecting it to work with your application. It's not a project I recommend for beginners, but if you are an extreme gardening geek like me, you'll understand why I raced to get as much in here as I could before going back to press and printing this special edition. Please keep me posted on your progress with this design by sending your emails to info@howtohydroponics.com - pictures are always appreciated!

Parts List

For simplicity's sake, we are going to use the same exact parts as the Dutch Bucket garden described in the previous chapter. The additional parts required are listed below.

(1-3 - depending on desired output) Nutramist Single head transducer modules

10' of 1/2" closed cell foam gasket tape for sealing lid

(1) 20-34 CFM (3"-4" Diameter) cooling fan, the type Radio Shack sells. 120VAC models are easier to work with but could prove hazardous around water if proper care is not taken to keep dry and isolated from contact with fog or condensation.

(1) 4" PVC 45 degree 'L' fitting and a short piece of 4" PVC to connect it to the reservoir - this must fit your fan, see step 1.

(1) 2' x 4' piece of 1/4" ABS or 3/4" heavy density foam board from which to cut the dutch bucker lids from. Foam is a lot easier to work with than ABS plastic which will require the use of a band saw to cut the lids and a hole saw to cut the cup holes - see Aerospring plans.

Since this modification utilizes the Dutch Bucket Garden's drain manifold as a fog injection manifold as well, you won't need any of the drip fittings, 1/2" tubing, water pump or growing medium that is used in the Dutch Bucket Garden. You may also need to make the legs of the stand 2-4" taller so that the fan assembly has clearance under the stand/drain manifold. You'll need the same tools as you would use for the Dutch Bucket Garden as well.

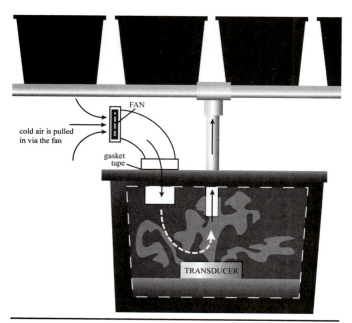

Fig. 1. The concept and operation is quite simple. An external fan forces fresh air into the reservoir where it mixes with the fog created by the transducer. Since this mixture can only escape through the drain manifold, it ends up filling the Dutch Buckets through their drain fittings. Excess solution that collects in the buckets drains back into the reservoir in the same tubing with no impedance to the fog.

Step 1. You'll need to find just the right fan (as specified in the parts list) that will fit neatly inside the PVC 'L'. Shown here is a 3.25" diameter fan inside the 4" PVC 'L'. It is held in place by the inner flange of the 'L' and sealed with some polyester batting to prevent escape of fog.

Step 2. Mount the fan as illustrated above. You'll then need to cut a hole in the lid of your reservoir that accepts the 4" PVC stub that you will insert into the opposite end of the 'L' Tracing the 4" PVC onto the lid is easy. Use a sharp razor knife to cut the hole so that you must pressure fit the PVC end through it. You should also use gasket tape around the seal to prevent any fog leakage.

Step 1/2

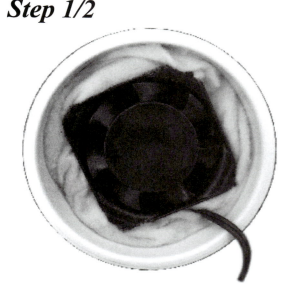

Step 3. Before inserting the fan assembly into the top of the reservoir, apply a piece of gasket tape around the hole where it will connect to help prevent fog leaks. Refer to Fig. 1.

Step 4. Apply gasket tape to the top of the reservoir to create an airtight seal exactly as done in the Aerospring plans. An airtight seal is also necessary between the lid and drain stem, so make sure to cut that hole extra snug.

Step 5. The Fog transducer sits inside a float which keeps it at an optimal operating level in the reservoir. I've had some luck routing the cord out between the junction where the gasket tape ends meet to form the seal. The triple fog transducers with Teflon-coated discs have a safety mechanism that shuts them off if the water level gets too low. Be advised, these powerful triple transducer modules can empty a small reservoir quickly.

Step 6. Cutting out appropriate lids from your choice of material will be a lot easier if you download the templates from www. howtohydroponics.com/fogger.html On the units I've built, Lexan was used for the lids only because it was at my disposal. After running some tests, high density foam seems to run cooler but gets a little cruddy after a couple of uses. If you choose foam, use the same method for making the lids as demonstrated in the plans for the Lettuce Raft.

Step 7. Install the Dutch Buckets onto the frame and manifold assembly, making sure their drains fit snugly into the manifold. This picture shows the fog being pumped through the drain manifold before the bucket is installed.

Step 8. Install just one of the 90 degree black drain adapters into each bucket, this will direct the fog across the inside of the Bucket and allow any excess condensate to drain back to the reservoir.

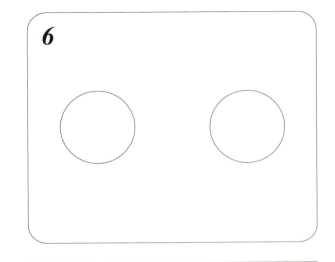

Download free printable Acrobat templates from: www.howtohydroponics.com/fogger.html

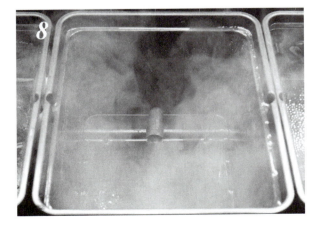

The Dutch Bucket Fogger Growers Guide

Growing medium

Voila! There *could* be none but in my grow trials, I found a definite benefit to using a very coarse medium like LECA stone or Aerolite in the bottom quarter of the buckets as it absorbed a little bit of moisture and acted as a buffer in case of a temporary fog failure. For this project, I have been using 3" net cups with a grow site plug to cap them off. In the site plugs, I drilled a hole just large enough to accept a #4 Perfect Starts plug or similar. By using the net cups beneath the site plugs, the roots take strong hold of the basket once they grow a bit offering the plant more physical support. For updates to or if you have trouble finding parts for this project,
check the website www.howtohydroponics.com/fogger.html for more info.

Planting

To start seedlings, I used a #4 Perfect Starts plug directly inserted in the site plug and placed them into 3" net cups as shown here. To start cuttings, you can use just the site plugs with a small keyhole cut in them as illustrated in the diagram below. I just got around to starting cuttings this way but didn't have time to get the pictures in here before re-printing this updated 4th edition. The results were spectacular. I've posted a template for a 12 site cloning lid in the same downloadable document.

Nutrition

Depending on your crop and stage of growth, you will want to choose a good quality sediment-free hydroponic nutrient. Do not use fertilizers designed for soil gardening as they do not contain a complete balance of nutrients required for growing this way. My own experiments have begun to show plants grow just fine with a half strength nutrient solution, this could be due to the increased root area.

Feeding cycle

I've had the most success running the fogger 24/7 as there's no margin for error. Don't forget the "no spray, your crops will turn to hay rule!" I can't stress how important it is to monitor your reservoir as the transducer will shut off if it runs low.

Maintenance

Keep the transducer discs clean. Using the triple Teflon coated transducer units will help in this department. Otherwise you will have to replace the discs frequently.

Aside from looking very interesting, aeroponic foggers like this one could make a dramatic difference in the way we grow. No mediums required, less nutrients wasted and of course, lower maintenance, that is if it works the way it's supposed to! Remember - this system IS a bonified experiment in pushing the envelope!

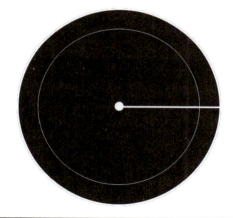

By drilling a small hole in the middle of the grow site plugs (also known as cup covers) you can insert cuttings in them. Be sure to cut the plugs as shown to allow removal of the cuttings once rooted. If a plant tried to grow to full term in a plug with such a small hole, the constriction that would result could get choked it off
.   Picture at left shows same sunflowers just 2 weeks after germination in our home-made fogging unit!!

The PVC Pipe Gardens

Shown here growing broccoli on the left and several varieties of leafy greens in the remaining three chambers. This system is extremely versatile and very popular with commercial growers looking to produce large harvests from small spaces both indoors and out.

My first encounter with a commercially available hydroponic system was a garden made by General Hydroponics from 6 inch PVC pipe. Since then, I've experimented with several variations on that design, in search of less expensive ways to get started in hydroponics. PVC pipe's inherent ease of use during construction, versatility, and availability as a plumbing product make it an ideal material for building your own hydroponic system. Standard round PVC pipe is available from any plumbing supply, and the newer square extrusions used here are available from construction material and outdoor fencing suppliers. The 5 inch square extrusions have the added benefit of increased stiffness, their flat bottoms prevent them from rolling over and they require less support than their 4 and 6 inch tubular counterparts. Before you get carried away trying to decide which type of PVC pipe to use for your system, remember that plants only care about food, water and proper oxygenation, and all of these designs do a good job of providing each of these requirements.

I prefer Roughtote® storage containers for nutrient reservoirs since they are made from FDA approved resins suitable for long term contact with food - their green and blue coloring keep algae growth to a minimum and they are virtually indestructible too.

Parts List

(1) 31 gallon Roughtote reservoir or similar
(4) 6 ft. PVC pipes (use either 4" or 6" round or 5" square type (used here)
(8) Endcaps (use rubber "Gem" caps on round pipe, PVC fence caps on square)
(2) Saw horse kits and whatever materials are required to assemble them.

(1) 700GPH or greater submersible pump or inline pump
Approx 5' of 3/4" PVC pipe for manifold construction
Approx 2' of 1/2" PVC pipe for cutting into spray line support clips
(25) feet of .375 ID poly spray line tubing
(4) 3/4" female garden hose swivel to compression adapters (for spray line ends)
(4) 10mm insert plugs to seal spray line ends
(4) 1" ID rubber grommets to seal spray line entry points into growth chambers
(4) 1 1/4" drain fittings (bulkhead fittings) or 1 1/4" drain pipe grommets (if grommets are used you will also need (4) 6" 1 1/4" PVC pipes for the level tubes.
(2) 3/4" PVC 'L' fittings
(4) 3/4" PVC 'T' fittings
(1) 3/4" female garden hose to 3/4" barbed fitting
(4) feet 3/4" I.D. opaque tubing (poly or vinyl - aquarium/drinking water safe)
(6) 3/4" slip to Male Hose Thread (MHT) to adapter

(1) 3/4" MHT cap
(1) small can PVC cement
(1) tube of aquarium safe silicone sealant
(2) 1" hose clamps

(1) 1/2" I.D. rubber grommet for sealing level tube exit
(1) 1/2" barbed elbow fitting for level tube assembly
(1) 1/2" rachet clamp for securing level tube on elbow fitting
24" of 1/2" blue or green poly tubing for level tube

(1) 3/4" high volume filter for keeping spray lines clear

(1) 4 Quart LECA stone 8-16mm (fills 20 - 3" cups)
Desired amount of 3" net cups - one for each plant site

The versatility of PVC pipes when used as growing chambers leave the possibilities endless. Here is a 3 foot model that provided me with fresh salad greens all winter long and kept the air in my home office comfortably humidified and fresh too!

Tools You'll Need

Electric or battery powered drill - 3/8" or 1/2" chuck
1 7/8", 2 7/8" & 4" hole saws for cutting drain holes, plant sites and service ports
5/8", 3/4" & 7/8" speed bore bits (flat, inexpensive drill bits)
1/8" drill bit to make spray holes in spray lines.
Hacksaw for cutting PVC pipe
Razor knife for cutting poly tubing
Ruler and a marker

Whether you choose four or six inch round PVC pipe or the new 5 inch square extrusions for grow chambers, the principal is the same. Plants are suspended in baskets while the upper part of their roots are treated to a fine spray as the bottom extremities are bathed in a constant flow of oxygen rich nutrient solution.

From top to bottom; 4" round, 6" round (both shown with rubber Gem caps installed - 6', 4.5' and 3' chambers made from 5 inch square PVC (end caps not shown on square chambers) The number and spacing of plant sites is entirely up to the grower making this design very versatile

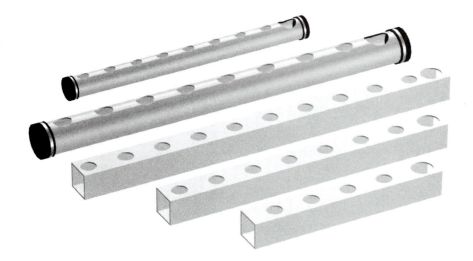

PVC Chambers Cross-Sections

blue arrows denote spray holes
green arrows denote nutrient flow

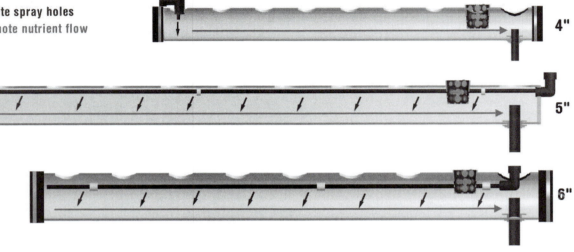

4"

5"

6"

PVC Chambers End-View

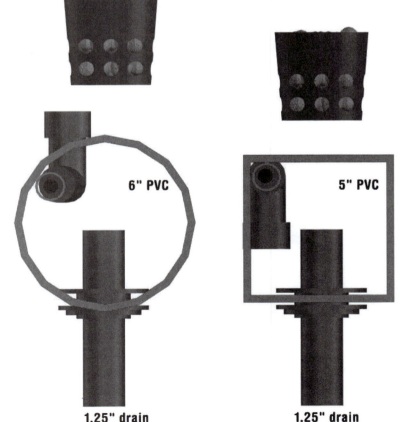

6" PVC

5" PVC

4" PVC

1.25" drain

1.25" drain

1" drain

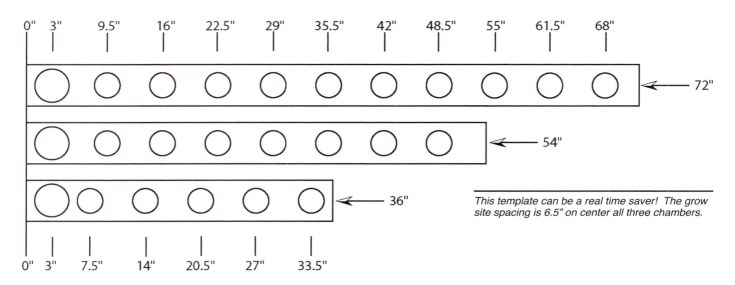

0" 3"   9.5"   16"   22.5"   29"   35.5"   42"   48.5"   55"   61.5"   68"

← 72"

← 54"

← 36"

This template can be a real time saver! The grow site spacing is 6.5" on center all three chambers.

0" 3" 7.5" 14" 20.5" 27" 33.5"

Step 1. Using either the template provided or your own design, you must first layout each of the holes to be cut. It is best to mark and measure them center to center. Make sure to pay close attention to avoid any mistakes which can be very costly in both time and materials.

Step 2. Using the 2 7/8" hole saw and a cordless drill to cut each of the grow sites and a 4" hole saw for the access ports (one per chamber, on right side of the chambers shown here) The 14v cordless drill I used here has cut hundreds of holes over the last year! A single charge was enough to finish the four chambers shown here each with 6 grow sites and 1 access port.

Step 3. The 5" and 6" growth chambers each have an internal spray line which needs to be suspended from the top of the chamber. To do this, cut spray line clips from the 1/2" PVC pipe - 3/4" to 1" long works best - use 3-5 per chamber and glue them exactly between the grow sites so as not to block the spay holes placed just off to the side of each grow site. The black arrow denotes how the spray line passes through each of the clips.

Cut 3/4" - 1" sections of 1/2" PVC pipe to make the spray line clips shown above. They are glued into the chambers using PVC cement. For best results, use PVC primer before applying glue to soften the material and provide a better glue joint.

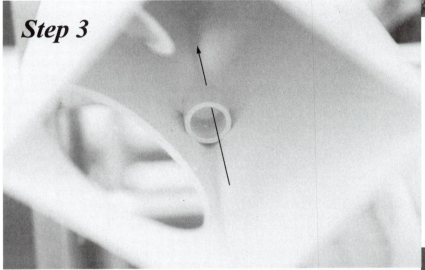

Step 3

Step 4. Endcaps for the 5" PVC chambers need to be glued on using PVC cement. Use PVC primer first on both surfaces to be glued. Stand the chambers on end and use a small squirt bottle to fill any gaps between the cap and chamber to prevent leaks.

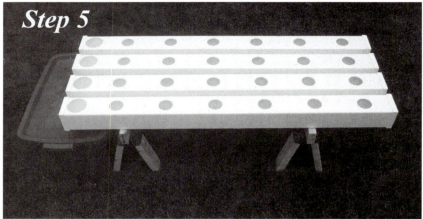

Step 5.

Step 5. Assemble your system so that each chamber is evenly spaced apart on the saw horse support. It is best to leave yourself a few inches of space between the bottom of the chambers and the lid of your reservoir. Measure the spacing from the center of one chamber to the center of the next to determine the spacing of spray lines on the manifold below.

Step 6. Layout the manifold parts as shown here and measure out the lengths of 3/4" PVC pipe you will need to complete the manifold. You may wish to refer to the next page for more photos of the complete manifold and how it attaches to the system for further clarification.

Step 7. Assemble the internal spray lines from the parts shown here - 3/4" FGH swivel adapter with a compression end, .375 ID poly spray line, 10 mm insert plug and a 1" rubber grommet to seal the entry point of the spray line into the growth chamber.

Begin by cutting the poly spray lines down to the exact inside length of your chambers. You will then need to use a 1/8" drill to puncture spray holes into each line just off to each side of every grow site. Keep the holes about a half inch from the grow sites so the don't get blocked by the spray clips installed in the previous steps.

Note. Once you insert the spray lines into the compression end of the adapters, they are nearly impossible to remove without damage. Test fit everything first! You only need to insert about 1/2" into the compression end for a good seal.

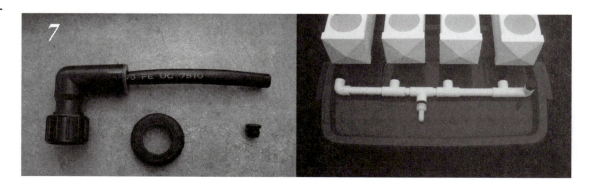

Step 8. Using a 1 3/8" hole saw, cut a hole into each of the endcaps to accommodate the spray lines. Center this hole exactly 1 1/8" down and 1 1/8" over from the same corner the spray line clips are attached. You will use a 1" I.D. rubber grommet (shown in the next step) to seal the compression fitting as it passes through this hole.

Step 9. Using a 1.5" hole saw, cut a hole for each chamber's drain fitting to mate with the lid of your reservoir. I have found the simplest way to measure and mark off the location for these holes is to connect all chambers to the injection manifold, position them over the reservoir and mark the center of each drain hole by sighting down each drain fitting.

Step 10. Connect your submersible pump as shown here using a length of vinyl tubing and a nylon barb to female hose thread adapter. I've had great success using the RIO series of submersible pumps with this garden design, Model 1100 shown here.

Step 11. A 7/8" hole in the bottom of the reservoir wall accepts a 1/2" ID rubber grommet, 1/2" barbed elbow and 1/2" blue level tubing to complete your nutrient reservoir level indicator

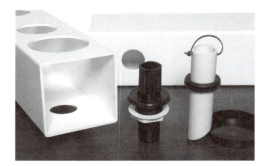

Note. There are actually two options available when making the drain stems. The first would be to use the bulkhead fitting and nut as shown at left, the second is to use a rubber grommet and 1 1/4" PVC stub. Cost and availability of the materials will help you decide as I've found both to work equally as well.

Step 12. If you choose to use the bulkhead fitting, be sure to seal with Aquarium-safe silicone sealant to prevent leaks. Apply as shown here. If you choose to go with the grommet method, it helps to apply a thin coating of nontoxic silicone grease to the inside of the grommet to allow the level tube to move up and down easily.

Step13. Assemble your stand from 2 saw horse kits and some 2x4 lumber. Use a level placed between the two saw horses to make sure the chambers will lay flat, with zero slope.

13a. Place the level across each sawhorse to make sure all the chambers will be at the same height.

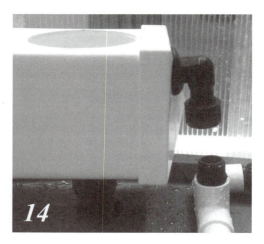

Step 14. You are now ready to connect the chambers to the injection manifold as shown in the sequence of photos here.

PVC Pipe Gardens - Growers Guide

Growing medium

Since this system is a pure water system, the only growing medium you will require is that to start your seeds or cuttings. Once you have viable plants, they will be placed into 3" plastic net cups with a handful of LECA stones to give the roots something to hold on to and keep them from falling over inside the cups.

Planting

Start your seeds or cuttings in your preference of starter cubes or sponges. Transplant to net cups once roots are clearly visible from the bottom of the cubes. Set plants in cups into your system make sure initial water level touches bottom of cups as shown in the middle photograph.

Nutrition

Depending on your crop and stage of growth, you will want to choose a good quality hydroponic nutrient. Do not use fertilizers designed for soil gardening as they do not contain a complete balance of nutrients required for growing in water. While you can successfully grow more than one type of plant in this system (ie vegetative, reproductive) for best results, choose one or the other this way you can target your nutrient solution to best satisfy its requirements.

Maintenance

Drain and replace nutrient in reservoir when it falls to a level just above the top of your pump. Never let your pump run dry. Inspect and clean in-line filters with every nutrient change. It's also a good idea to clean the chambers and reservoir between crops to remove any sediment or algae that can sometimes build up in high light conditions. Use a scrub brush and a 10% solution on bleach. Rinse thoroughly!

Storage

Drain reservoir and use to feed your landscaping or lawn. If using LECA stone or gravel, dump into a storage container and rinse thoroughly and allow to dry. Clean all empty buckets cups and chambers with hot water and allow to dry before storing.

The AutoPot

If Tomatoes could talk, what do you think they'd have to say about how well they're being fed in this picture courtesy AutoPot UK

The secret to the AutoPot system is the AQUA valve which automatically subirrigates the tray containing the pots ONLY when needed without any waste whatsoever. Best of all, the AutoPot is completely powered by gravity, so it does not need any electrical pumps or power!

The AutoPot is a gravity-fed hydroponic system that delivers just the right amount of nutrient and water to each plant, automatically. To do this, the AutoPot relies on a patented device called the AQUAvalve. While there are several configurations of planters and gardens that employ the AQUAvalve, my favorite is a double tray planter that uses 2.2 gallon pots nestled in a recessed tray that houses the AQUAvalve. This method of hydroponics is called sub-irrigation and it has many important benefits over other technologies. What I have found to be the foremost benefit of the AutoPot is that nutrient management is a thing of the past! Since nutrient solution is never recycled in the system, adjusting pH and refreshing "old" nutrient solution is no longer necessary. In fact, since the AutoPots use a medium like soil, coir, perlite or rockwool grow cubes (or combination thereof), plants are afforded an additional buffer against nutrient and pH fluctuations. Research has even shown a 45% reduction in nutrient requirements for this type system. My own experience with AutoPot has been excellent, and its flexibility allows for creating a totally customized system you can design and build on your own. You can grow 1 to 1000 plants with the same system by simply adding modules to expand your garden.

The AQUAvalve actually operates similar to a float valve in a toilet bowl! It opens to flood the tray to a one inch depth, and then it seals off the supply to stop the flow. The growing medium then wicks the nutrient solution to provide for the plant. Unlike a float valve that would reopen once the water level drops, the AQUAvalve employs a mechanism to prevent it from opening until the tray is completely dry. Since the growing medium stores moisture, it will slowly begin to dry as the plants draw upon it. But the AQUAvalve is already in action, once again supplying fresh nutrient solution to your plants to keep them happy and healthy. I have found the magic of this system is not so much the functioning of the AQUAvalve, but the action it creates in the growing medium. During the wet cycle, stale oxygen is displaced from the medium as it wicks up fresh nutrient solution. As the medium dries, fresh oxygen is drawn in to revitalize the root zone. The AQUAvalve mimics the cycle of natural rainfall.

A simple, bare bones AutoPot system will consist of: (a) reservoir of suitable size (use 1 to 4 gallons of capacity per tray depending on size of plant, rate of growth and environmental conditions); (b) 1/4" tubing; (c) a 1/4" valve to close off unused AutoPots from the reservoir; (d) 1/4" 'T's to connect two or three AutoPots to each 1/4" line; (e) a 1/4" compression grommet to connect the 1/4" lines to the reservoir; (f) the AutoPot "pots" (two per tray); (g) a valve cover; (h) the AQUAvalve; and (i) the AutoPot tray. I've illustrated several configurations below that should help you plan and build an AutoPot system that best suits your needs.

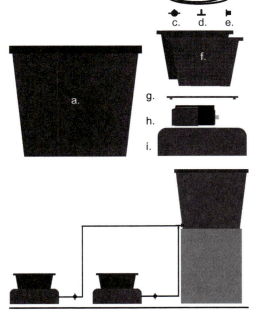

A. Rigid PVC pipe use 10/32" threaded joiners with teflon tape

B. Soft Poly tubing use .16" double barb joiners w/ silicone sealant

A system with one or two trays can be fed by 1/4" tubing and a small reservoir raised a foot or two above the top of the pots. When expanding beyond 4 modules, it is wise to use 1/2" supply line to reduce friction and increase the capacity of the tubing to feed the trays. Rigid PVC or flexible poly may be used, the different pipes require unique connectors to attach the AutoPots.

1/2" 'L' fitting w/ 1/2" grommet

1/2" blue tubing (level indicator)

40-50 gallons

1/2" 'T' fitting w/ threaded stem and valve

1/2" filter

1/2" poly tubing or rigid PVC

raise reservoir 2 ft.

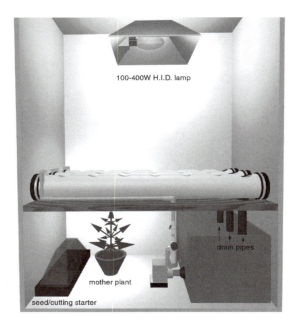

100-400W H.I.D. lamp

mother plant

seed/cutting starter

drain pipes

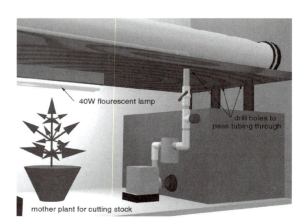

40W flourescent lamp

drill holes to
pass tubing through

mother plant for cutting stock

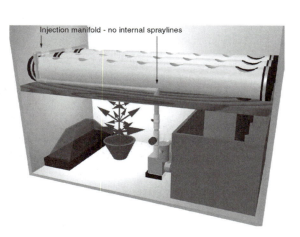

Injection manifold - no internal spraylines

Gardening Indoors

The Spare Closet Garden

If you live in an area where space outdoors is tough to come by, here are some ideas for creating a "closet garden." In the example shown, the six inch PVC system is custom fit inside this available space. You will find that this configuration works well for maintaining a steady supply of salad greens, herbs and flowers by virtue of the two-level arrangement. On the lower level, a fluorescent light of 40 Watts is used to start seedlings and root cuttings that are kept inside the 10"x20" humidity domed flat at lower left. If you wish to take cuttings for speedier growth and more solid stock, you can use the remaining area for growing a "mother" plant, which is used for the sole purpose of providing cuttings. Once the cuttings or seedlings are well rooted, you can easily transplant them to the upper part of your closet for placement into your modified PVC system and exposure to the High Intensity Discharge (HID) lamp. WARNING: Be very careful to keep your lamp at least 24" from all surfaces, walls and ceiling. Installing a small vent fan in the ceiling is also a necessity, because heat will build up quickly. Use the type commonly found in bathrooms - 100-150 CFM (cubic feet/ minute) should be fine for most small areas.

If you do a careful job of blocking light between the upper and lower halves, you can force flower your favorites by reducing the daylight hours of operation to 12-14 hours per day. While your flowers are blooming on top, your next crop can be rooting below. On a system this small, you can save a lot of hassles by leaving out the internal spray lines and using the same method of injection that the four inch PVC system uses. That is simply a direct spray down and into the chamber. Use a strong chain secured to a stud in the ceiling to support the light and allow you to raise or lower it according to the height of your crop.

In the example on this page we use the self watering

Enjoy fresh fruit & flowers when there's a foot of snow outside!

AutoPots to create a nice little pepper and tomato garden from a spare closet in the garage. This system is designed to be very low maintenance and with a 5 gallon gravity fed reservoir which has been lasting about 4-5 days between fill-ups. I started the peppers from seed and the tomatoes were given to me by a customer, they looked a little sickly at first, but after a week in the AutoPots, they got their color back and caught right up to the peppers. The layout of this system allows plants to grow to heights of 30-36" and features forced ventilation and a shaded nursery/reservoir area that keeps stray light from reaching the main production area. I also used a 2" thick foam board to insulate the plants from the cold concrete floor. HID lamp on a pulley system, ballast on shelf to keep the heat away from the plants and close to the exhaust fan.

Bell peppers and cherry tomatoes grow like weeds under the 400W metal halide super sun system. When the fruits begin to set, we will change to 400W HPS and change to a "bloom" feeding regimen to promote fruit development.

The author built this simple 8x12' greenhouse in his yard in just a few weekends and for less than $1200 in lumber and GE Thermoclear glazing.

The Do-It-Yourself Greenhouse

If you are at all handy with a hammer and saw, consider building your own greenhouse. You can find many plans on the web by doing an internet search for "greenhouse plans." It's a project that will take two people a weekend or so to complete and it can give you 10 to 20 years of service if you use quality materials. Erecting any kind of structure on your property may require review by the zoning board, especially if you are building on a concrete slab. If a review or variance is required, the town which will usually ask your closest neighbors if they object. For this reason, I visited my neighbors before breaking ground to fill them in on my plans. Needless to say, I wound up with several additional mouths to feed. Little did they know I'd be feeding them anyway. After all, it's a hydroponic greenhouse!

The Prefabricated Greenhouse

More and more companies are catching on to the market demand for affordable, hobby-style greenhouses. One of those companies, RION, has designed a clever line of full-sized, prefabricated greenhouses that can be shipped by UPS. From what I've heard, they snap together in a couple hours and out last many of their treated wood counterparts. For just a little more than you would spend on plans, lumber, glazing and hardware, you can get up and growing in one of these nifty prefab houses in a fraction of the time, and never worry about rotting wood and termites to boot.

In this 4x12' lean-to style house, PVC chambers were mounted like giant window boxes to facilitate short stature crops like lettuce and basil without cramping or casting shade on other plants inside.

The Professional Greenhouse

Over the years I have worked with several people who had the pleasure of being able to afford a professionally designed and manufactured greenhouse by one of the many custom builders in the states. What makes these glass houses "professional" level is: (a) they are built of structural steel and/or aluminum and glass rather than wood; (b) sometimes insulated glass is used, if required. The higher rigidity of aluminum and steel versus wood allows thinner sections to be used in the construction, which increases the amount of light that reaches plants. Professionally built greenhouses are almost always erected on a solid concrete foundation that in most places requires that permits and zoning variances are applied for ahead of time. Many of these houses are available in varying widths and lengths and with a selection of trimmings like finial posts and aluminum roll up shutters, as shown in the picture of a Texas Greenhouse.

Conclusion

Hydroponics is rapidly gaining momentum and popularity as the best way to cultivate everything from flowers and food to medicine. In Europe, hydroponics is now widely accepted by consumers and is quickly catching on in other countries around the world. By now you should be well on your way to harvesting your first crop of hydroponic produce. I hope that I have answered all of your questions, and I have provided you with a strong understanding of the hydroponic method. Please feel free to email me with any comments/ suggestions and mistakes I may have missed so I can make the necessary corrections.

Since the Hydroponic industry is still rather small, and there aren't many local shops at which to purchase supplies, we've established an on-line garden store that specializes in hydroponic garden supplies and even prefabricated gardens for those of you who can't wait to get started! In cooperation with some of the best companies in the industry, we are constantly striving to include a complete selection of components, nutrients and accessories that you may require to build and maintain the gardens featured in this publication. If you can't find it at your local hydroponics retailer, ask them to give Futuregarden a call so we can supply them with the products you need or visit us online at www.howtohydroponics.com/interactive
Good Luck and Happy growing!

Keith Roberto

Email your questions to
asktheauthor@howtohydroponics.com
and I'll be happy to answer
them as time permits.

Index

Symbols

no entries

A

absorption 14
aerobic 37
Aeroponics 24
aeroponics 13
African Violet 50
air scrubbers 57
Algae 58
algae 15
Aloe 7
anaerobic 37
Aphids 60
asphyxiation 15
AutoPot 96
AutoPots 25
Aztecs 12

B

Babylon 12
Ballast 44
Basil 46, 50
Beans 50
biodegradable 18
biodegradeable 16
biological contro 60
Boron 29
botanical 6, 10
Botrytis 57
breeding 9
Broccoli 50
Bromeliads 42

C

Calcium 28
calcium 11
Capsicum 50
Carbon 26, 27
Cattleya 50
CELSS 13
Chicory 50
Chillies 51
Chive 46

Chlorophyll 28
Chrysanthemums 42
cloning 53
CO2 21, 38, 49
Cobalt 29
coco 13
coconut 17
coconut coir 17
Cocopeat 17
compounds 6
Copper 29
copper 57
Cucumber 50
cultivation 12
cutting 9
Cymbidium 50

D

Damping off 58
damping off 57
DE 58
deficiency 29, 36
dehydrated 15, 52
deionized 11
Denrobium 50
diatomaceous earth 58
Dieback 15
Dill 46
disease 56
Dissolved Oxygen 49
dissolved oxygen 24
Distilled 11
Dutch Bucket 22

E

EC 50
Eggplant 50
EGS 24
Egyptian 12
Ein Gedi System 24
Electrical Conductivity 50
Electrical conductivity 50
elements 6
embryo 51
Encarsia formosa 60
Endive 50
enzyme 29

Epcot 13
evaporation 12
excretion 10

F

F1 7
F1 Hybrid 7
fertigation 7
filters 57
fluorescent 40
force flower 98
fungi 56
fungicide 57
fungistat 57
fungus gnat 58
Fusarium 37

G

genetic 7
Geolite 18
Gibsofilia 42
Gladiolia 42
Gold 26
gravel 13
gravity-fed 96
gray mold 57
greenhouse 100
greenhouse gas 38
Grorox 18

H

Habanero 47
hardness 11
HID 40
High Pressure Sodium 44
hormone 17
hormones 53
HPS 14, 44
humidistat 57
Humidity 49
Hybrid 7
hybrids 7
Hydrofarm 41
Hydrogen 26, 27
Hydroponics 12
Hydroton 18

I

incandescent 40
indigenous 7
infestation 56
inhibit 42
intensity 41
interstitial spaces 16
ionic 14
Iron 28

J

no entries

K

KISS 21

L

Lacewings 60
Lady bugs 60
Lamp cord 44
larvae 56, 58
LECA 18
Lettuce 50
Light 49

M

Magnesium 29
Manganese 29
Marjoram 46, 50
Mealybugs 59
medicine 6
medium 13
Melon 50
membranes 14
meristem 58
metabolism 13
Metal Halide 44
Methane 37
MH 44
microbes 10
microbiological 37
mildew 56
Mint 46, 50
molds 56
molecules 26
molt 59

See what you've mist!

CYCLONE
ULTRASONIC FOGGER
BY NUTRAMIST

Instant Humidity

Pest Control Fogging

Drip-Free Foliar Feeding

Fungicides/Mildecides

Improved Propagation

APPLICATIONS INCLUDE

FOGPONICS

When traditional hydroponic/aeroponic methods are combined with a gentle fog, upper air roots receive the benefits of having unlimited access to oxygen, stimulants and supplements. The result is a superior root system.

HUMIDIFICATION

The Nutramist Fogger can also be used to provide additional humidity in the grow room and greenhouse as the ultra-fine fog vaporizes entirely within seconds after release.

PROPAGATION

Whether you're starting from seeds or cuttings, once the initial roots emerge from your starting medium, growth explodes. The accompanying photo shows a habanero pepper seedling just 36 hours after sprouting from a seed.

PEST CONTROL

The idea of using the Nutramist ultrasonic fogging mechanism to create a more effective delivery method for direct acting pest controls has been extensively researched and documented.

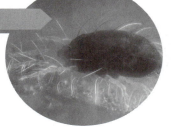

FOLIAR FEEDING

Foliar treatments are literally inhaled by leaves since the Nutramist fog is so fine. Leaves are never left soaking wet which prevents dreaded mildew and mold outbreaks.

MYCOLOGY

Growing mushrooms indoors is a challenge. Humidity, temperature and cleanliness of the air in the environment must be strictly controlled. Nutramist can help mycologists gain better control over their craft.

DEALERS WANTED   info@nutramist.com   888-338-3305   www.nutramist.com

CE, TUV listed low-volt power supply for safe operation • ABS, PP & stainless steel components • Only 45W consumption • 16-22 Oz/Hr output

pure

success

From simple beginnings, great things grow.

genhydro.com

©2014 GH

UNDER CURRENT™ PRO

GREENHOUSE GRADE
RECIRCULATING WATER
CULTURE SYSTEM

CURRENT CULTURE H2O

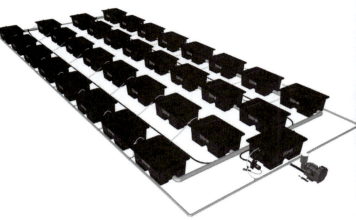

MADE FOR COMMERCIAL GROWERS

The redesigned **Under Current™ PRO** represents the largest, highest quality, most durable version of our **Under Current™** system to date. With high levels of aeration and circulation, nutrient efficiency is maximized and yields are expected to be off the charts.

The 35 gallon **Under Current™ PRO** systems will function much like their 8 and 13 gallon counterparts but will feature several unique and up-sized heavy duty components. Every element of the system has been reinforced and maximized for longevity in adverse greenhouse-style conditions.

GROWING IN THE UNDER CURRENT™ PRO

For commercial applications the **Under Current™ PRO** triumphs in efficiency and yields. The PRO system offers growers the opportunity to fill very large spaces and grow massive plants without the extra work of managing multiple systems and reservoirs. Having fewer larger systems equals higher productivity in terms of workflow, transplanting, maintenance and harvesting.

The **Under Current™ PRO** system would be best situated in either a greenhouse or indoors with a combination of vertical and horizontal lighting. The 35 gallon PRO growth module with single plant sites will be best utilized on 70"+ plant centers. Starting plants in our 8 gallon **Under Current™** systems and transplanting them to the PRO module at a height of 3-4' will yield a monstrous 8-10'+ finished plant when harvested.

For even more flexibility we offer interchangeable PRO Lids in 4, 6 and 11-site configurations. These durable ABS lids increase the PRO system's versatility and allow for tighter plant spacing, quicker turnaround times and Sea of Green (S.O.G) style cultivation methods.

GREENHOUSE GRADE PRO COMPONENTS

PRO GROWTH MODULE: The reinforced solid ABS PRO Growth Module features water level indicators, recessed bulkhead coves, easy drain bottom, recessed drain valve cove and custom inlets for our float valve and water inlet tee. Made in CA.

PRO LIDS: The reinforced solid ABS PRO Lid allows growers to easily transfer plants from our 8 or 13 gallon systems by simply moving our standard CCH2O Lid and CCH2O Net Pot intact. The PRO Lid will also be available in a 4-site, 6-site and 11-site version for tighter plant spacing and Sea of Green cultivation. All four PRO Lids incorporate dual port-hole access points and air inlet coves. Made In CA.

AQUA-PORE PRO XL AIR DIFFUSERS: All PRO systems come standard with our new Aqua-Pore PRO XL Air Diffusers. Aqua-Pore Pro Diffusers have low back pressure creating significantly higher oxygen transfer rates and higher dissolved oxygen (DO) levels. The membrane's tiny pore size creates extremely small diameter bubbles. These new diffusers are more durable, have a long life, require low maintenance and feature a quick connect fitting for easy installation.

More info @ www.cch2o.com

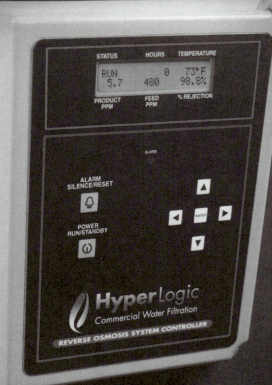